$59.95

Atlas
of
Anatomy

Elke Lütjen-Drecoll
Johannes W. Rohen

Atlas
of
Anatomy

The Functional Systems of the Human Body

by **Elke Lütjen-Drecoll**
and **Johannes W. Rohen**

With 439 figures, 405 in color

Williams & Wilkins
A WAVERLY COMPANY

BALTIMORE • PHILADELPHIA • LONDON • PARIS • BANGKOK
BUENOS AIRES • HONG KONG • MUNICH • SYDNEY • TOKYO • WROCLAW

Prof. Dr. med. Elke Lütjen-Drecoll
Prof. Dr. med., Dr. med. h. c. Johannes W. Rohen
Anatomisches Institut II der
Universität Erlangen-Nürnberg
Universitätsstr. 19
D-91054 Erlangen/Germany

Authorized translation of the 1st German language edition
Lütjen-Drecoll, Rohen: Atlas der Anatomie
© 1997 by F. K. Schattauer Verlag GmbH, Stuttgart, Germany

To purchase additional copies of this book, call o
customer service department at **(800) 638-0672** or f
orders to **(800) 447-8438.** For other book services, i
cluding chapter reprints and large quantity sales, ask f
the Special Sales department.
Canadian customers should call **(800) 665-1148** or f
(800) 665-0103. For all other calls originating outside
the United States, please call **(410) 528-4223** or fax us
(410) 528-8550.
Visit Williams & Wilkins on the Internet:
http://www.wwilkins.com or contact our customer servi
department at **custserv@wwilkins.com.** Williams
Wilkins customer service representatives are availab
from 8:30 am to 6:00 pm, EST, Monday through Frid
for telephone access.

Copyright © 1998 by
Williams & Wilkins
351 West Camden Street
Baltimore, Maryland 21201-2436 USA

Rose Tree Corporate Center
1400 North Providence Road
Building II, Suite 5025
Media, Pennsylvania 19063-2043 USA

Library of Congress Cataloging-in-Publication Data
Lütjen-Drecoll, Elke.
    [Atlas der Anatomie, English]
    Atlas of anatomy : the functional system of the
    human body / Elke
Lütjen-Drecoll, Johannes W. Rohen.
        p. cm.
    Includes index.
    ISBN 0-683-30641-3
    1. Human anatomy--Atlases. I. Rohen, Johannes W
    (Johannes Wilhelm) II. Title.
    [DNLM: 1. Anatomy atlases. QS 17 L973a 1998]
QM 25.L9313 1998
611'.0022'2--dc21
DNLM/DLC
for Library of Congress   98-23048 CIP

Composing, printing, and binding:
Mayr Miesbach, Druckerei und Verlag GmbH,
Am Windfeld 15, D-83714 Miesbach, Germany

Printed in Germany
                    98 99 00 01
    1 2 3 4 5 6 7 8 9 10

Preface

After the success of our Color Atlas of Anatomy: A Photographic Study of the Human Body for medical students and clinicians we were asked to create a smaller atlas particularly suitable for students of allied professions and for people who are generally interested in learning something about structure and function of the human body. This was a difficult task since the basic knowledge, interests, and needs vary widely among this potential readership. Under no circumstances did we merely want to create an abridged version of our big atlas. In contrast, we decided to develop a new concept for this book that was focused predominantly on the illustration of the functional systems of the body rather than on the descriptive and regional anatomy alone. Most comparable books or atlases are based on schematic, mostly simplified drawings which often reflect reality only in a limited way. The third dimension is usually lacking. Therefore, we decided to depict photos of the actual anatomic specimens. This has the advantage of conveying the real object with its correct dimensions. Since the photos themselves are normally difficult to understand for students of allied or nonmedical professions we added corresponding explanatory drawings to indicate the essentials of the respective structures. Thus, we hope that we offer the reader a brief insight into the complicated morphology of the different functional systems of the human organism. To present photos and illustrations in a comprehensible way without requiring the reader to study complicated textbooks beforehand, we included brief explanations. This should, however, not be misinterpreted. This atlas was never intended to replace a textbook but rather to serve the reader as a visual aid in mastering more complicated and elaborated texts, commonly used in courses of nursing and allied health curricula.

For a better understanding of the functional systems of the body and the needs of the daily clinical work we also included some brief explanations of the microscopic structures and added a few selected pictures obtained with modern diagnostic imaging modalities.

Studies of the complexity of the functional anatomic systems are always fascinating since they reveal the breathtaking beauty and overwhelming grandness of the human body itself and also become the fundamental base for insights into our spiritual being. These studies eventually form the framework of our humanity.

Erlangen, April 1998   Elke Lütjen-Drecoll
                                                                              Johannes W. Rohen

Acknowledgments

The majority of the anatomical specimens newly depicted in this atlas were dissected with great skill and knowledge by Dr. Keishi Okamoto (University of Nagasaki/Japan) during his stay in Erlangen, as well as Dr. Martin Rexer and Mr. Jeffrey Bryant, both members of our staff. We like to express our gratitude for their encouragement and enthusiasm. We also like to express our many thanks to Prof. Winfried Neuhuber (head of Department of Anatomy I, University of Erlangen) and Mr. Tony Simpson for their great efforts in supporting our work.

The CT-scans and MR-images were kindly provided by the Siemens AG, Erlangen, as well as by Prof. W. J. Huk (University of Erlangen) and Dr. A. Heuck (University of Munich). We are also greatly indebted to Mr. Hans Sommer (SOMSO Co., Coburg) who provided a number of excellent natural human bone specimens.
Excellent pictures were also kindly provided by Prof. G. Rettinger (University of Ulm), Prof. H. H. Tulusan (University of Bayreuth), and Prof. K. V. Hinrichsen (University of Bochum).
In addition, we would like to express our great gratitude to our photographer, Mr. Marco Gößwein, who contributed the excellent macrophotos; and to our skilled artists, Mrs. Annette Gack and Ms. Heike Schmidt, who produced not only many new excellent drawings but completed also the elegant layout of this book. We are also greatly indebted to our secretary, Mrs. Lisa Köhler, for her untiring work in writing the text and Ms. Christine Wiesler (Lörrach) for her excellent help with the English translation.

Finally, we would like to express our sincere thanks to all coworkers for their help and advice, but particularly to Mr. D. Bergemann and Dr. W. Bertram of the publishing company Schattauer, for their stimulation and great support of this work.

Content

Prefixes _____

a-, an-	= without		infra-	= underneath, below
ab-	= away from		inter-	= between, among (intercostal)
ad-	= toward, added to, near		intra-	= within a part of a structure (intracranial, intraocular)
ante-	= before, forward		intro-	= into, within
anti-	= against		juxta-	= next to (juxtaglomerular)
antero-	= position ahead of or in front of (anterior to)		mes-, mesa-,	= middle, midline
bi-	= two, double, twice		meso-	(mesencephalon, mesentery)
circum-	= around, surrounding, about		meta-	= beyond, after (metacarpus)
contra-	= opposite, against		para-	= near, beside (parametrium, parathyroid)
cost-, costo-	= rib (intercostal)		peri-	= around, beyond (pericardium, perichondrium)
de-	= away from, from		post-	= after, behind
di-	= double		prae- (pre-)	= before, in front of (prenatal)
dia-	= through, across (diaphragm, diaphysis)		pro-	= in front of, before (prosencephalon)
dis-	= separate from, apart		retro-	= backward, located behind (retroperitoneal, retrocecal)
e-	= out, away		semi-	= partial, half (semilunar)
endo-	= within, innermost (endocardium)		sub-	= under, beneath (subclavian artery)
epi-	= on, upon (epidermis)		super-	= above, over
ex-, exo-	= outside, away from (excretion, exocrine)		supra-	= location above or over (suprarenal)
extra-	= beyond, outside of, in addition		syn-	= with, together
hemi-	= half (hemisphere)		trans-	= across, beyond
hyper-	= above, over, excessive (hypertonic)		ultra-	= excessive
hypo-	= under, deficient, below, beneath (hypogastrium)			

Directions _____

Anterior	= in front of, ventral		Medial	= relating to the midline
Basal	= pertaining to the base		Median	= a vertical plane dividing the body into right and left halves; situated in the middle
Caudal	= pertaining to any tail-like structure; inferior in position		Palmar	= pertaining of the palmar side of the hand
Cranial	= toward the head		Plantar	= pertaining of the sole of the foot
Deep	= profundus		Posterior	= toward the back, dorsal
Dexter, dextra	= right		Proximal	= nearer to the origin of a structure (e.g. the trunk)
Distal	= farther from the origin of a structure or from a given reference point		Sagittal	= in an anteroposterior direction
Dorsal	= toward the back, posterior		Sinister, sinistra	= left
Frontal	= pertaining to the forehead		Superficial	= over, above, excessive
Inferior	= below, lower		Superior	= above, upper
Lateral	= farther from the midline of the body		Transverse	= lying across, horizontal
			Ventral	= toward the belly, anterior

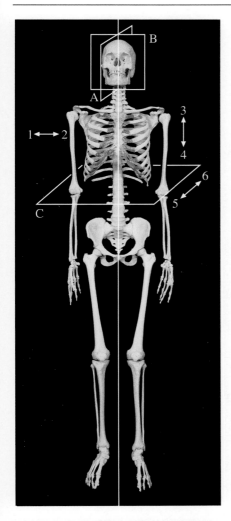

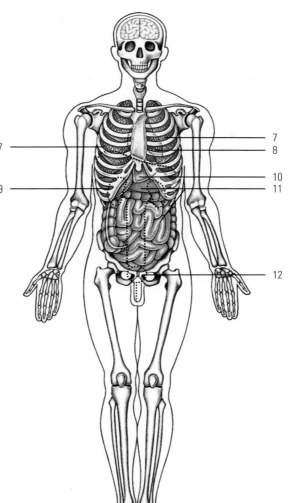

Body planes and sections:
A Sagittal section. The midsagittal (or median) section passes through the body axis
B Frontal (or coronal) section divides the body into anterior and posterior parts
C Transverse (or horizontal) section divides the body into superior and inferior parts.

General directions:
1 Lateral (located to one side)
2 Medial (located toward the midline – opposed to medial)
3 Proximal (nearest to the midline – opposite of distal) or cranial (towards the head)
4 Distal (farther from the midline to the trunk) or caudal (toward the tail)
5 Ventral (more anterior)
6 Dorsal (more posterior).

Organs
7 Lung
8 Heart
9 Kidney
10 Liver
11 Gastrointestinal tract
12 Urinary bladder

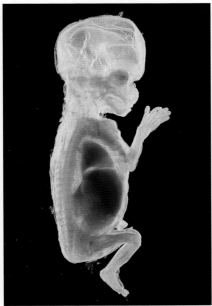

Human fetus (at 3rd month) (isolated, slightly stained and cleared). After the 3rd month, the human embryo is termed fetus.

The human body shows three characteristic formal principles. The basic form at the head is spherical, whereas the prevalent form at the limbs is radial. Thus, the principle of polarity is predominant. The horizontal dimension (right-left side) is dominated by the principle of mirror image (bilateral) symmetry. In the front-back dimension another formal principle is realized, namely the principle of segmentation. The trunk can be divided in equally formed sections, called segments. Each segment consists of a pair of bones, muscles, vessels and nerves of similar or equal shaping (e.g. thorax).

The organs of the three main functional systems are situated differently within the three great cavities of the body: the brain in the cranial cavity, the circulation and respiratory organs working rhythmically in the thoracic cavity, and the metabolic and excretory organs (gut, liver, kidneys) in the abdominal cavity.

The embryo develops this basic structure at a very early stage in form of the three germ layers. The anlage of all functional systems is already completed after four weeks. During the first two months of pregnancy the unborn child is called an embryo, from the third month until birth it is called a fetus.

Methods. Today, the structure of the human body can be examined not only by means of anatomical dissections, but also in the living organism (so-called diagnostic imaging modalities). In addition to X-ray or Roentgen-ray imaging, the method of X-ray computed tomography (CT) has been developed imaging object sections in multiple directions. In contrast, in magnetic resonance imaging (MR) the computed data are obtained from a large high-power magnet allowing object sections in multiple directions. Ultrasound diagnosis is based on the principle of reflecting sound waves on structures of differing densities.

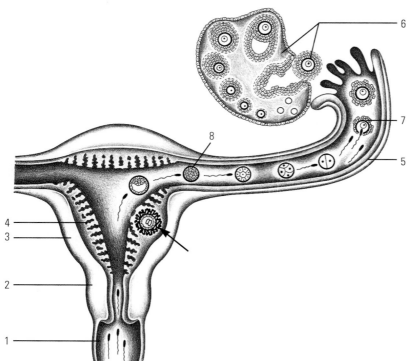

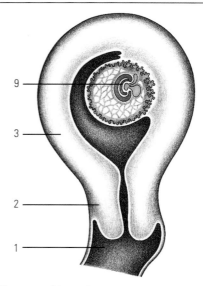

Uterus with embryo at day 21. The villous chorion surrounds entirely the embryonic disc (9). Beginning of the development of neural tube.

Uterus, uterine tube, and ovary showing the ovarian cycle, fertilization and human development during the first week. After ovulation (6), the ovum enters the uterine tube (5) where fertilization (7) can take place. The zygote undergoes a series of rapid cell divisions, called cleavage, forming the morula (8), which reaches the lumen of the uterus. The morula converts into the blastocyst which attaches to the uterus wall, where it is implanted at the 6th day. Arrow = beginning of the development of germ layers around 12th day.

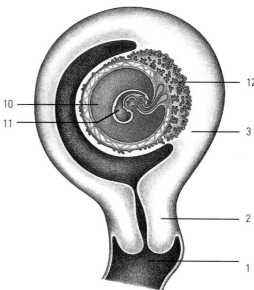

Uterus with embryo (around 4th week). Embryonal body and placenta are formed; the amniotic sac is still relatively large.

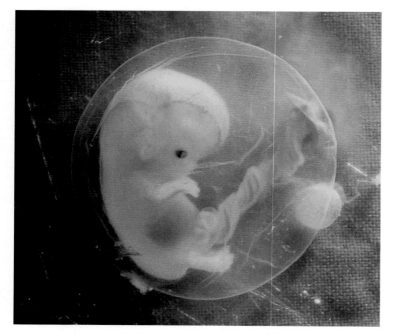

Human embryo within the amniotic sac (27 mm CR, day 54). Note the umbilical cord, the connection between embryo and placenta (not visible) (courtesy of Prof. K. V. Hinrichsen, from Human Embryology, Springer Verlag, Berlin, 1990).

 1 Vagina
 2 Cervix of uterus
 3 Uterus
 4 Mucous membrane of uterus with glands
 5 Uterine tube
 6 Ovary in the stage of ovulation
 7 **Fertilization** (sperm cell enters the ovum)
 8 Morula
 9 Embryonic disc (development of neural tube)
10 Amniotic sac (lined by amnion and chorion)
11 Anlage of nervous system
12 **Placenta**

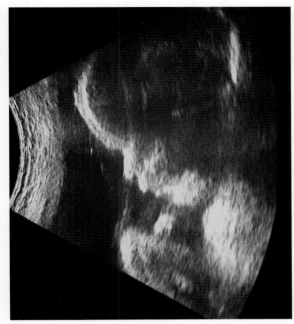

Ultrasound image of a human fetus (5th month). Face, shoulder, and hands are well discernible (courtesy by Prof. Tulusan, Bayreuth, FRG).

In the course of embryonic growth, the development of the head is completed first. The face shows human characteristics as early as the 8th week. From the 9th week on, the brain has reached a stage of development in which the embryo already demonstrates twitching movements and reflexes.

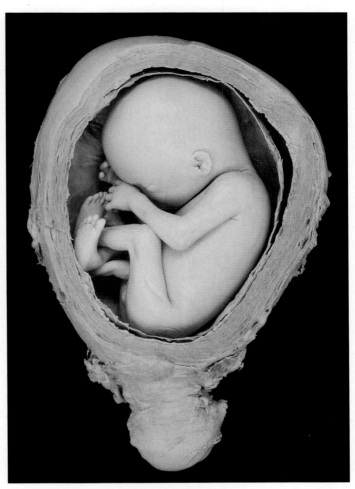

Human fetus within the uterus (5th month). The uterine neck is completely closed. It does not open before birth.

Stages of embryonic development	
days 1–4	Fertilization, cleavage in uterine tube, formation of morula
day 6	Implantation begins
[days 12–14]	First lack of menstrual bleeding
day 17	Development of three germ layers
day 21	First anlage of nervous system
day 22	Heart begins to beat
day 26	Arm bud becomes apparent
day 28	Embryo measures 4.0 mm (CR)
day 35	Embryo measures 8.0 mm (CR)
9th week	Fetal development begins, reflectoric movements of arms and legs become visible
38th–40th week (days 266–280)	Birth

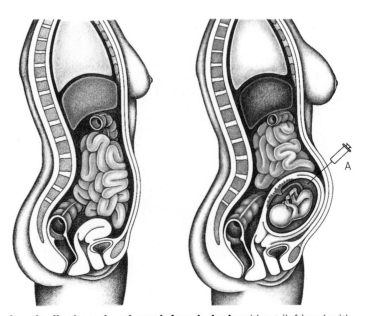

Longitudinal section through female body without (left) and with pregnancy (right). Note the compression of abdominal organs during pregnancy. A = puncture of amniotic sac (amniocentesis).

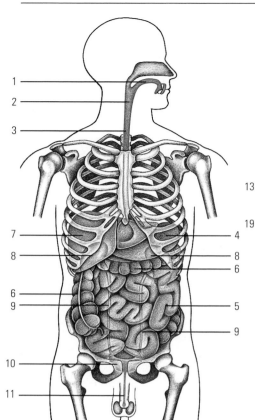

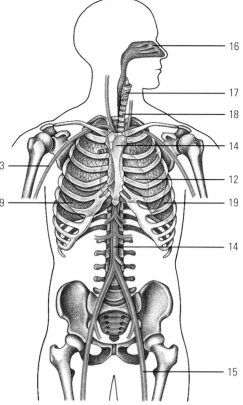

Digestive system
1 Oral cavity
2 Throat (pharynx)
3 Esophagus
4 Stomach
5 Small intestine
6 Large intestine (colon)
7 Liver

Urinary system
8 Kidney
9 Ureter
10 Urinary bladder
11 Urethra

Circulation system
12 Heart
13 Brachial artery
14 Aorta
15 Femoral artery

Respiratory system
16 Nasal cavity
17 Larynx
18 Trachea
19 Lung

Nervous system
20 Brain
21 Cerebellum
22 Spinal cord
23 Sympathetic trunk
24 Vagus nerve
25 Intercostal nerves
26 Celiac ganglion
27 Autonomic nerve plexus

Endocrine organs
28 Pituitary gland (hypophysis)
29 Thyroid gland and
   parathyroid glands
30 Adrenal gland
31 Testis (male gonad)

Sagittal section of the body
32 Thorax and ribs (costae)
33 Diaphragm
34 Liver
35 Small intestine
36 Vertebral column
37 Aorta
38 Heart
39 Muscles of the back
40 Uterus
41 Vagina

Digestive and excretory system. Their organs are mainly located within the abdominal cavity. Digestive system (including oral cavity, esophagus, liver, gut, etc.) appears green, the excretory system (kidney, ureter, bladder, etc.) red.

Respiratory and circulation system. Their organs are mainly located within the thoracic cavity. Respiratory system (lung, nasal cavity, trachea, etc.) appears blue, heart and blood vessels red.

A = cranial cavity
B = thoracic cavity
C = pericardial cavity
D = abdominal cavity
E = pelvic cavity

Cavities of the body. The thoracic cavity lined by the pleura contains the two lungs and the heart, which is located within the pericardial cavity. The abdomino-pelvic cavity is lined by the peritoneum. Cranial cavity and vertebral canal contain brain and spinal cord surrounded by the protecting meninges.

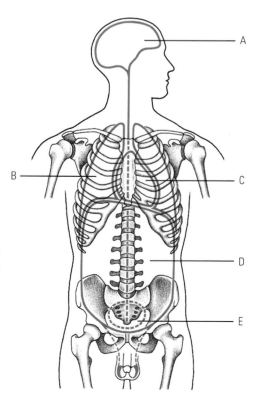

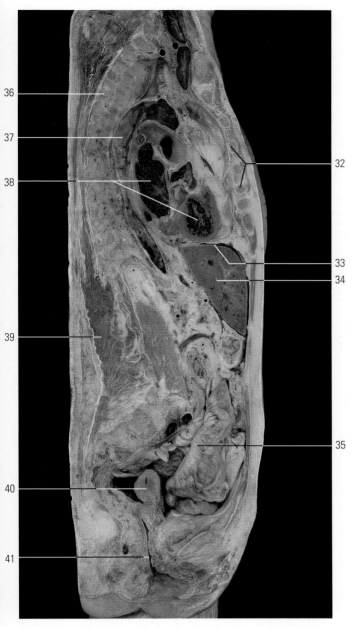

Sagittal section through the trunk (42-year-old female). Note the location of organs within the thoracic and abdominal cavity, which are separated by the diaphragm. The section is slightly paramedian so that the vertebral canal is not visible.

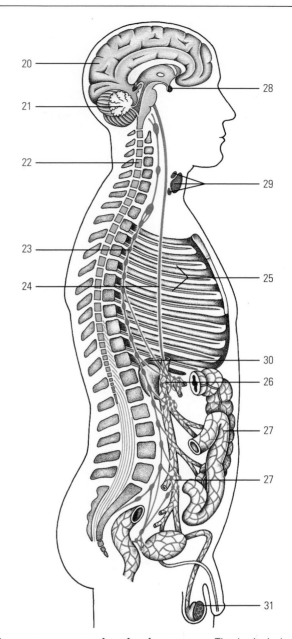

Nervous system and endocrine organs. The brain is located within the cranial cavity, the spinal cord is situated within the vertebral canal (note the segmental organization of the latter). The autonomic nervous system receiving nerve fibers from the sympathetic trunk and vagus nerve forms plexus and ganglia within the abdominal cavity.

In the human organism, three great **functional systems** have developed. The main organs of each of these three systems are situated in one of the respective cavities of the body.

1. The **metabolic system** comprises all organs that are responsible for the nutrition, digestion, regeneration, and excretion of substances. It comprises mainly the digestive system (gastrointestinal tract, liver, etc.), the excretory system (urinary system) and the reproductive system (a special case of excretion).

2. Rhythmic functions (cardiac rhythm, respiratory rhythm) are predominantly a feature of **the cardiovascular system and the respiratory system.** Both those systems act as a mediator between the nervous system on one hand and the metabolic system on the other.
3. The **sense organs, nervous system,** and **endocrine organs** form a system where the exchange of information and the control of body functions are predominant. Its function is the perception, processing of and response to the different kinds of information received from within the body and from the external environment.

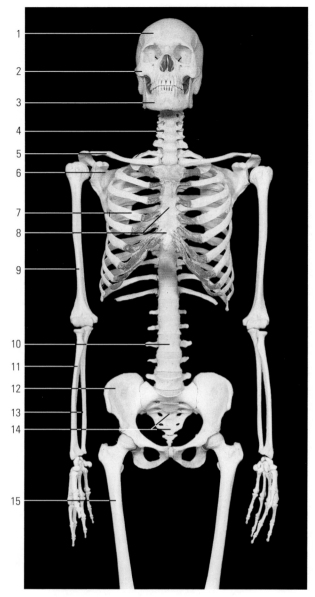

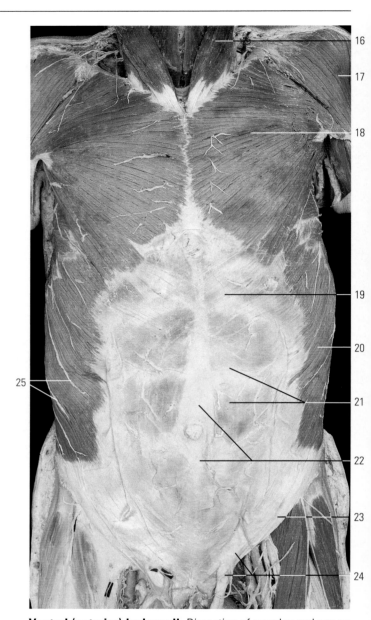

Human skeleton (anterior view). Note the segmental organization, the bones of the trunk (vertebrae, ribs, etc.), and the radial structure of the extremities. In contrast, the skull reveals a spherical form.

Ventral (anterior) body wall. Dissection of muscles and nerves (superficial layer). Note the segmental organization of the cutaneous nerves (see schematic drawing on page 9, lower-left).

1 Sternocleidomastoid muscle
2 Maxilla
3 Mandible
4 Cervical vertebrae
5 Clavicle
6 Shoulder blade (scapula)
7 Thorax
8 Sternum
9 Humerus
10 Lumbar vertebra
11 Radius
12 Pelvis
13 Ulna
14 Sacrum
15 Femur

16 Sternocleidomastoid muscle
17 Deltoid muscle
18 Pectoralis major muscle
19 Anterior sheaths of rectus abdominis muscle
20 External oblique muscle
21 Rectus abdominis muscle with tendinous intersection
22 Linea alba
23 Inguinal ligament
24 Spermatic cord and inguinal canal
25 Cutaneous nerves
26 External intercostal muscle
27 Internal intercostal muscle
28 Transverse abdominal muscle
29 Sheath of rectus abdominis muscle
30 Spermatic cord

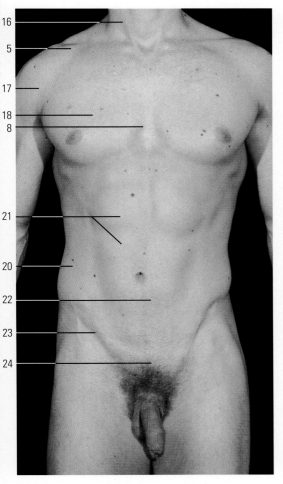

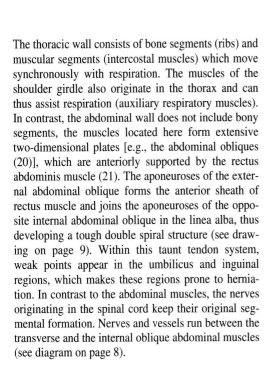

Human body (anterior view, male). The rectus abdominis muscle is contracted and prominent (see schematic drawing on the left).

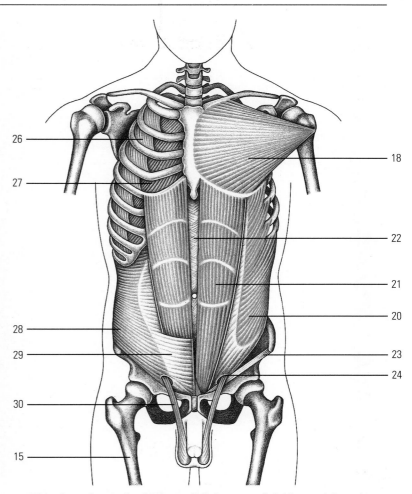

Muscles of anterior body wall (left = superficial layer, right = deeper layer). The anterior rectus sheath has been removed with the exception of the lower-right portion.

The thoracic wall consists of bone segments (ribs) and muscular segments (intercostal muscles) which move synchronously with respiration. The muscles of the shoulder girdle also originate in the thorax and can thus assist respiration (auxiliary respiratory muscles). In contrast, the abdominal wall does not include bony segments, the muscles located here form extensive two-dimensional plates [e.g., the abdominal obliques (20)], which are anteriorly supported by the rectus abdominis muscle (21). The aponeuroses of the external abdominal oblique forms the anterior sheath of rectus muscle and joins the aponeuroses of the opposite internal abdominal oblique in the linea alba, thus developing a tough double spiral structure (see drawing on page 9). Within this taunt tendon system, weak points appear in the umbilicus and inguinal regions, which makes these regions prone to herniation. In contrast to the abdominal muscles, the nerves originating in the spinal cord keep their original segmental formation. Nerves and vessels run between the transverse and the internal oblique abdominal muscles (see diagram on page 8).

Region	Form of body wall	Content	Regenerative capacity
Head (cranial cavity)	closed bony system	brain, sense organs	nearly not
Thoracic cavity	segmental organization (muscles and bones)	heart, lungs, etc.	small
Abdominal cavity	no bones, but muscles	liver, intestine, etc.	high
Pelvic cavity	incomplete	excretory and reproduction systems	production of germ cells

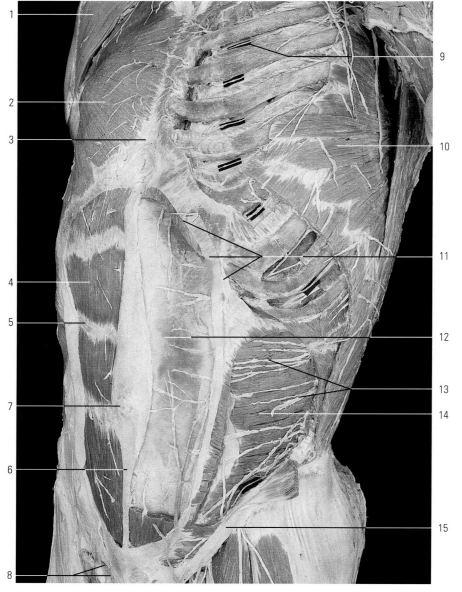

1 Deltoid muscle
2 Pectoralis major muscle
3 Sternum
4 Rectus abdominis muscle
5 Tendinous intersection
6 Linea alba
7 Navel (umbilicus)
8 Inguinal canal
9 Intercostal nerves (located underneath the ribs)
10 Serratus anterior muscle
11 Costal arch
12 Posterior sheath of rectus abdominis muscle
13 Intercostal nerves (10th-12th thoracal segments)
14 Transverse abdominis muscle
15 Inguinal ligament
16 Internal oblique muscle
17 External oblique muscle
18 Anterior sheath of rectus abdominis muscle
19 Sternocleidomastoid muscle
20 Pectoralis minor muscle
21 Cremaster muscle
22 Heart
23 Liver
24 Spinal cord and canal
25 Trachea
26 Vertebral column, thoracic part

Muscles and nerves of the trunk (right = superficial layer, anterior layer of rectus sheath has been removed; left = deeper layer, external and internal oblique and rectus muscles have been removed).

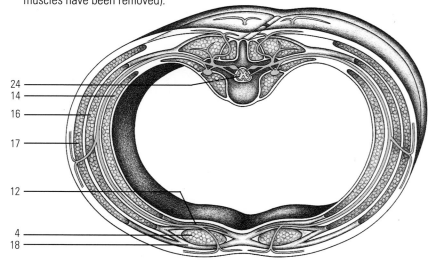

Cross-section through the body wall (from above), showing the layers of the abdominal wall and its innervation by branches of spinal nerves (yellow).

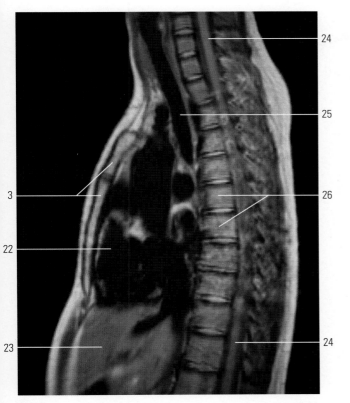

Median sagittal section through the trunk (MR-image). The thoracic cavity contains the heart (22) with great vessels such as the aorta. Within the vertebral canal, the spinal cord (24) is discernible.

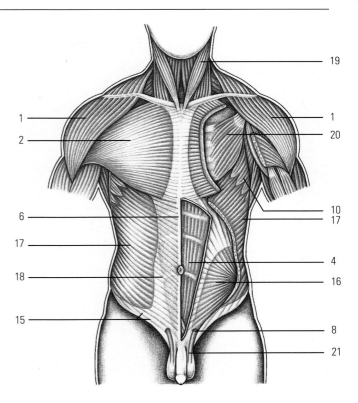

Muscles of the anterior body wall (right = superficial layer, left = deeper layers). Muscle fibers of the internal abdominal oblique (16) extend to the cremaster muscle (21) of the testis.

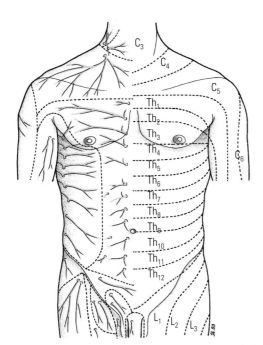

Segmental arrangement of cutaneous nerves of the anterior body wall. C₃–C₆ = cervical, Th₁–Th₁₂ = thoracal, L₁–L₃ = lumbar segments.

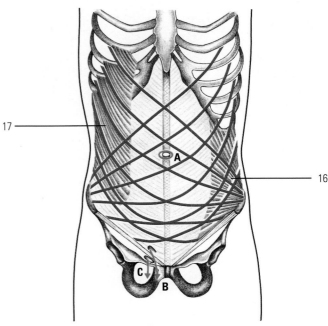

Architecture of tendon fibers of the two abdominal oblique muscles in the rectus sheaths. The crossing zone forms the linea alba. Red = openings for herniae (A = site of umbilical, B = of inguinal, C = of femoral herniae).

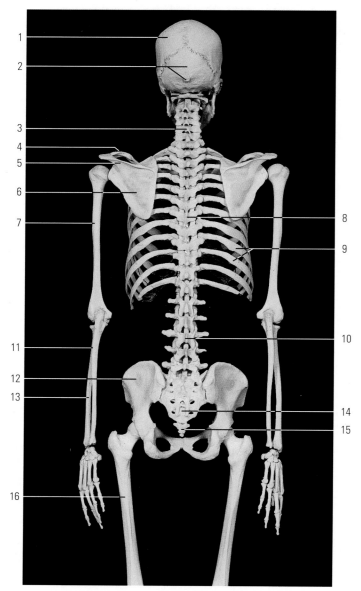

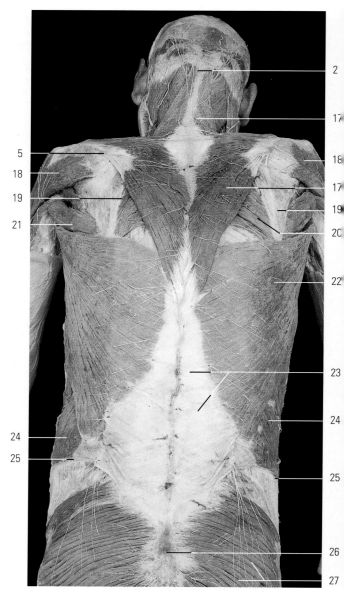

Human skeleton (posterior view). Note the segmental organization of the bones. The transverse processes of lumbar vertebrae (10) are remnants of ribs.

Muscles and nerves of the back (superficial layer). Note the segmental arrangement of cutaneous nerves (see drawing on plate 11).

1 Skull (parietal bone)
2 Skull (occipital bone with external occipital protuberance)
3 Vertebral column, cervical part (consisting of 7 cervical vertebrae)
4 Clavicle
5 Spine of scapula
6 Shoulder blade (scapula)
7 Humerus
8 Vertebral column, thoracic part (consisting of 12 thoracic vertebrae)
9 Ribs (thorax comprises 12 ribs or costae)
10 Vertebral column, lumbar part (consisting of 5 lumbar vertebrae)
11 Ulna
12 Pelvis (here: Ilium)
13 Radius
14 Sacrum
15 Coccyx

16 Femur
17 **Trapezius muscle**
18 Deltoid muscle
19 Vertebral border of scapula
20 Rhomboideus major muscle
21 Teres major muscle
22 **Latissimus dorsi muscle**
23 Thoracolumbar fascia (surrounding the deep back muscles)
24 External oblique muscle
25 Iliac crest
26 Sacrum
27 **Gluteus maximus muscle**
28 Splenius capitis muscle
29 Sternocleidomastoid muscle
30 Lesser rhomboid muscle
31 Levator scapulae muscle
32 Inferior posterior serratus muscle

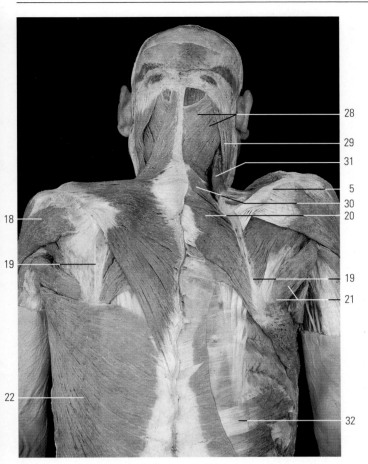

Muscles of the back (left = superficial layer; right = deeper layers).

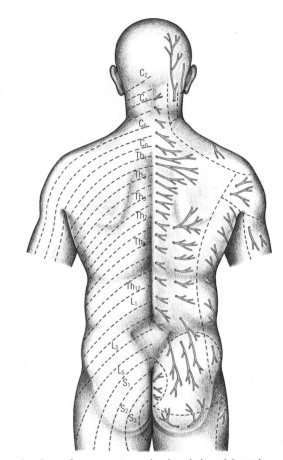

Organization of segments and related dorsal branches of spinal nerves at the back.

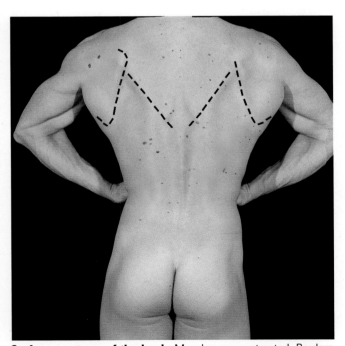

Surface anatomy of the back. Muscles are contracted. Borders of trapezius muscle and shoulder blade are marked.

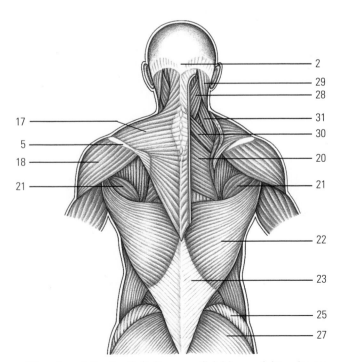

Muscles of the back (left = superficial layer, right = deeper layer of shoulder muscles).

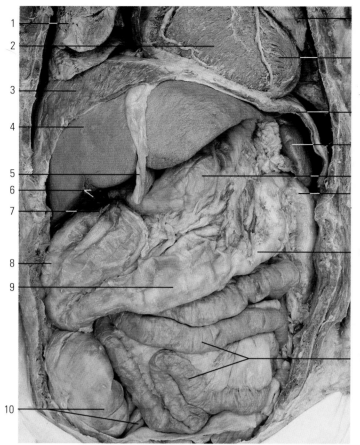

Abdominal organs (anterior view). Anterior abdominal wall and greater omentum have been removed.

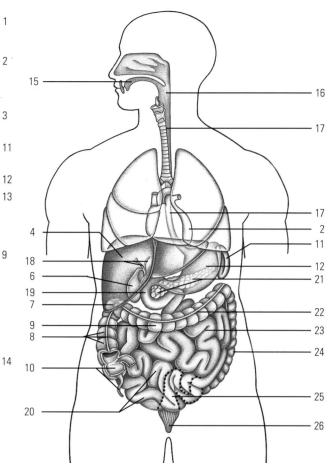

Survey of the main organs of the digestive system (schematic drawing).

Gastrointestinal tract	Main functions
1. Oral cavity with salivary glands	Chewing, moistening of food, tasting, initiation of carbohydrate digestion
2. Esophagus	Bolus transport by peristaltic waves
3. Stomach	Temporary storage of food, initiation of protein digestion
Small intestine	
4. Duodenum with pancreas and liver	Digestion of carbohydrates, proteins and lipids
5. Jejunum	Absorption of nutrients
6. Ileum with Peyer's plaques	Reabsorption of fluid and solutes, immune response to food antigens
Large intestine	
7. Cecum with vermiform appendix	Reabsorption, immune response
8. Colon	Absorption of sodium and water, incubation of bacteria, elimination of wastes
9. Rectum	Reabsorption, retaining of feces
10. Anal canal	Defecation

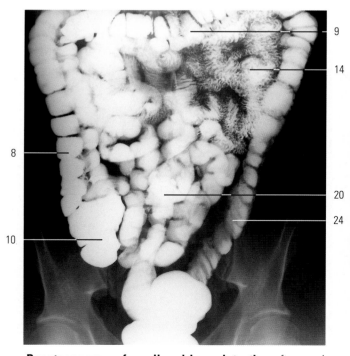

Roentgenogram of small and large intestine after swallowing of contrasting matter.

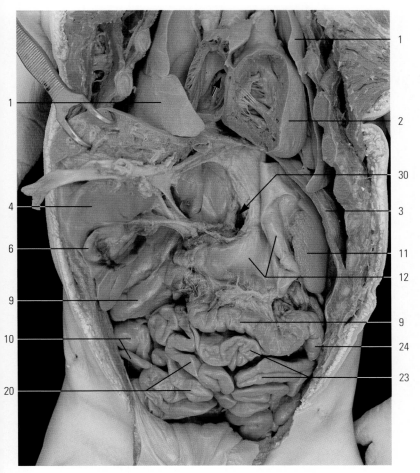

1 Lung
2 **Heart**
3 Diaphragm
4 **Liver**
5 Round and falciform ligament of liver
6 **Gallbladder** (vesica biliaris)
7 Right colon flexure
8 Ascending colon
9 Transverse colon
10 Colon cecum with vermiform appendix
11 **Spleen**
12 **Stomach**
13 Left colon flexure
14 **Small intestine**
15 Oral cavity
16 Throat (pharynx)
17 Esophagus
18 Extrahepatic bile ducts
19 **Duodenum**
20 Ileum (small intestine)
21 **Pancreas**
22 Tenia of colon
23 Jejunum (small intestine)
24 Descending colon
25 Sigmoid colon
26 Rectum
27 Small omentum (omentum minus)
28 Great omentum (omentum majus)
29 Uterus and vagina
30 Lesser sac (bursa omentalis)
31 Mesentery

Abdominal organs of the fetus. The liver (4) has been divided and reflected to display the lesser sac (30). Lesser and greater omenta have been removed. Note the foramen ovale (arrow) of the heart (2).

The **digestive system** is mainly situated in the abdominal cavity. Liver, stomach, and pancreas lie in the upper abdomen, which is partly protected by the lower thorax. At the pylorus, the stomach continues into the C-shaped duodenum attached to the posterior abdominal wall. The excretory ducts of both, the pancreas and liver (common bile duct), lead to the descending part of duodenum (19). In contrast to the duodenum, the small intestine (jejunum and ileum) (20, 23) is freely movable within the abdominal cavity, but fixed to the posterior abdominal wall by the mesentery (31). The large intestine (colon, 8, 9, 24) forms a sort of garland enclosing the small intestine. The transverse colon is mobile and yet attached only at the mesentery (mesocolon). In the pelvic cavity, the sigmoid colon (25) extends into the rectum (26) and the anal canal.

Sagittal section through the abdominal cavity in the female. The small ▶ intestine is fixed to the dorsal abdominal wall by the mesentery (31). The great omentum (28) fixed to the transverse colon covers the small intestine anteriorly. The lesser sac (bursa omentalis) (30) is located behind the small omentum (27) and the stomach (12). Red = peritoneum.

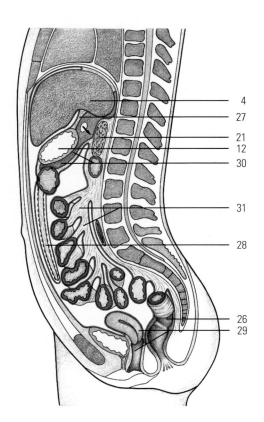

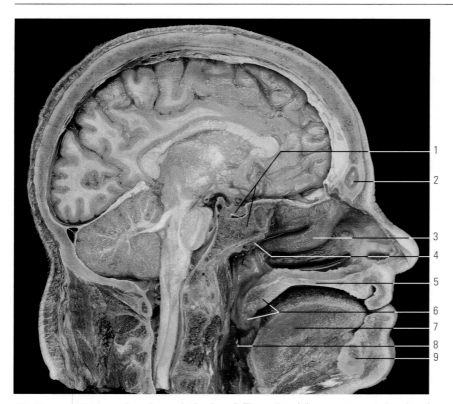

1   Sella turcica with pituitary gland
2   Frontal sinus and bone
3   Medial nasal concha
4   Pharyngeal tonsil
5   **Hard palate**
6   **Soft palate** and **uvula**
7   Tongue
8   **Throat (pharynx)**
9   Mandible
10 **Palatine tonsil**
11 Auditory tube and tonsil
12 **Epiglottis**
13 Larynx (vocal fold)
14 Esophagus
15 Vestibule of mouth (oral cavity)
16 Root of tongue and **lingual tonsil**
17 Hyoid bone
18 Circumvalate papillae
19 Arytenoid cartilage
20 Cricoid cartilage and posterior cricoarytenoid muscle
21 Trachea
22 Filiform papillae
23 Fungiform papillae
24 Foliate papillae at lateral wall of tongue
25 **Taste buds** with innervation

Median sagittal section through the head. The palate (5) separates nasal and oral cavities from each other. The throat (pharynx) (8) is the site where respiratory and digestive tracts cross. Note the location of the pituitary gland at the sella turcica (1) and the angle of clivus at the base of the skull.

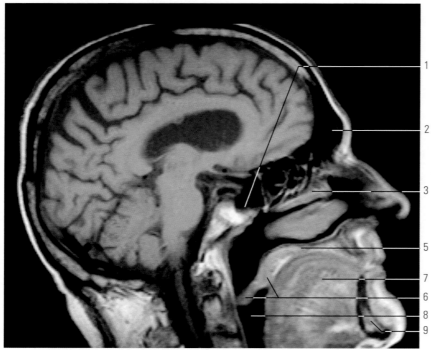

Median sagittal section through the head (MR-image) (compare with the anatomical section above).

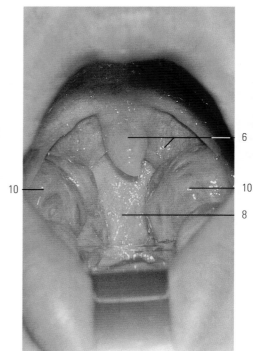

Posterior part of oral cavity in vivo (child, 11 yrs. old). Note soft palate with uvula (6) and palatine tonsil (10).

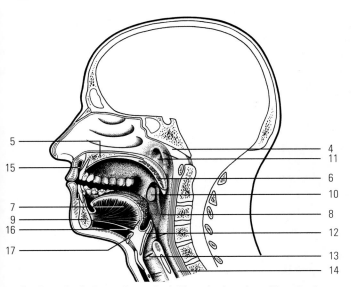

Oral cavity (schematic section). Note the location of lymphatic tonsils (blue) at the transition zone towards the pharynx (so-called lymphatic ring of Waldeyer).

Mucous membrane of tongue with two types of papillae (vallate and foliate papillae) containing numerous taste buds (25) (red).

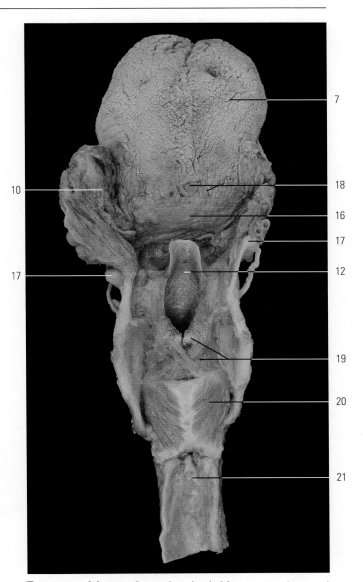

Tongue and larynx (posterior view). Mucous membrane of pharynx and esophagus have been removed to display epiglottis (12) and posterior laryngeal muscles.

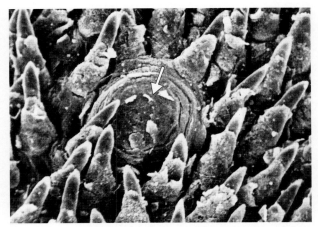

Scanning electron micrograph of tongue surface (×30) showing numerous filiform papillae and one fungiform papilla (arrow).

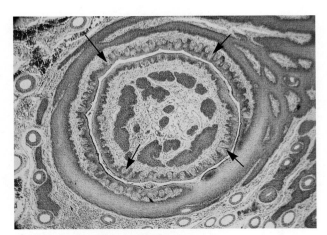

Light micrograph of a vallate papilla of the tongue (tangential section, ×38). Note the numerous taste buds within the epithelial lining (arrows).

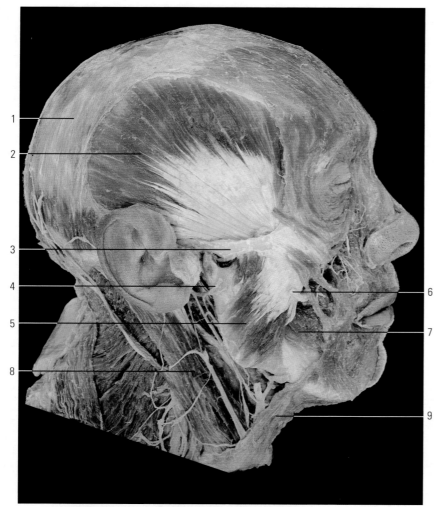

1   Galea aponeurotica
2   Temporalis muscle
3   Zygomatic arch
4   Facial nerve (n. VII)
5   Masseter muscle
6   Parotid duct
7   Buccinator muscle
8   Sternocleidomastoid muscle
9   Platysma muscle
10 Temporomandibular joint
11 Head of mandible
12 External acoustic meatus
13 Mandible
14 Maxilla
15 Coronoid process of mandible
    (insertion of temporalis muscle)
16 Articular disc
17 Buccalis nerve
18 Lateral pterygoid muscle
19 Maxillary artery
20 Medial pterygoid muscle
21 Lingual nerve
22 Inferior alveolaris nerve and vessels
    (for teeth of the mandible)
23 Gingiva (gum)
24 Cementum
25 Dentin
26 Pulp
27 Periodontal ligament
28 Lamellar bone
29 Pouch of gingiva
30 Branches of infraorbital nerve

Muscles of mastication I (temporalis and masseter muscles, lateral view). The parotid gland has been removed.

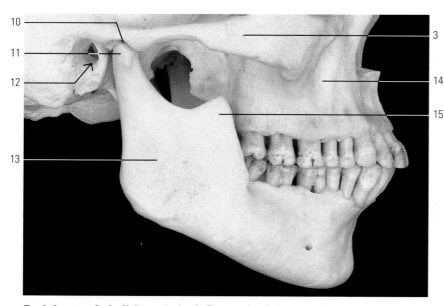

Facial part of skull (lateral view). The teeth of the upper jaw protrude slightly from those of the mandible (so-called prognathy).

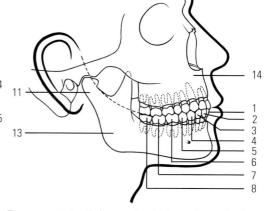

Permanent teeth (approximate time of eruption):
1   Central incisor (≈ 7 yr)
2   Lateral incisor (8 yr)
3   Canine (11 yr)
4   First premolar (11 yr)
5   Second premolar (11 yr)
6   First molar (6-7 yr)
7   Second molar (12-13 yr)
8   Third molar (17-22 yr) (wisdom tooth)

Muscles of mastication
1 Temporalis muscle
2 Lateral pterygoid muscle
3 Medial pterygoid muscle
4 Masseter muscle
Supra- and infrahyoid muscles
5 Mylohyoid muscle
6 Sternohyoid muscle
7 Thyrohyoid muscle
8 Sternothyroid muscle

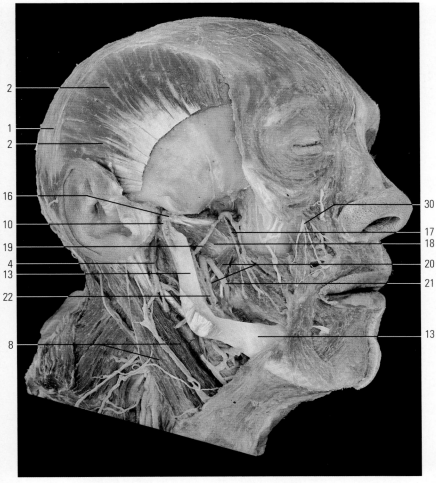

Muscles of mastication II with temporomandibular joint. Zygomatic arch, mandible and temporalis muscle have been partly removed to display the lateral pterygoid muscle (18) the tendon of which is connected to the articular disc (16) of the joint.

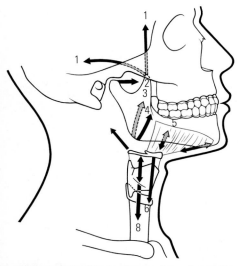

Location and effect of muscles of mastica-tion, supra- and infrahyoid muscles.

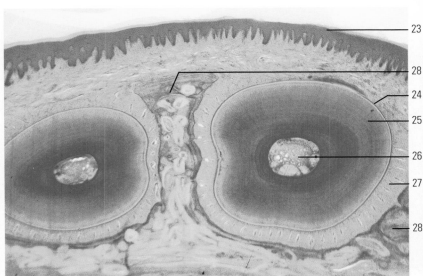

Horizontal section through the mandible showing the roots of two teeth (25) with periodontal sheath (27) (light micrograph, × 17).

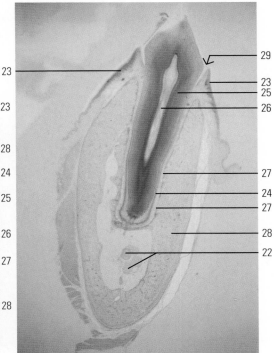

Longitudinal section through mandible with tooth (central incisor, light micrograph, × 4.5). Enamel dissolved.

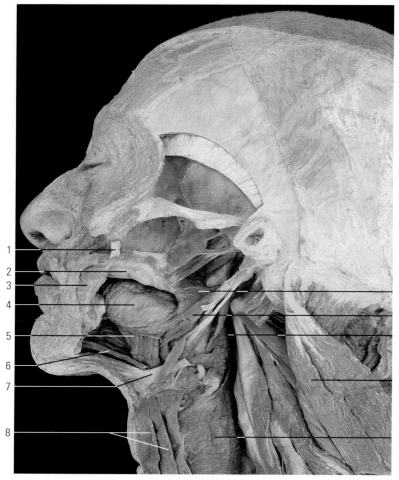

1   Parotid duct
2   Maxilla (without teeth)
3   Buccinator muscle
4   Tongue
5   Hyoglossus muscle
6   Mylohyoid muscle
7   Hyoid bone
8   Infrahyoid muscles
9   Superior constrictor muscle of pharynx
10   Styloglossus muscle
11   Middle constrictor muscle of pharynx
12   Sternocleidomastoid muscle
13   Inferior constrictor muscle of pharynx
     (continuous to esophagus)
14   **Parotid gland**
15   Sublingual caruncle
16   Sublingual gland
17   Submandibular gland
18   Masseter
19   Mandible
20   Cervical vertebra
21   Temporalis muscle
22   Common carotid artery
23   Vagus nerve (n. X) (supplying thoracic and
     abdominal organs with parasympathetic nerves)
24   Trachea
25   Aortic arch
26   **Esophagus**
27   Stomach, cardia portion
28   **Solar plexus** (autonomic nervous system)
29   Sympathetic trunk
30   Diaphragm
31   Liver
32   Pancreas
33   Autonomic nervous plexus of stomach
34   Uvula

Transition of oral cavity into the pharynx. Mandible and buccinator muscle (3) have been partly removed and sternocleidomastoid muscle (12) reflected. The upper jaw has no teeth.

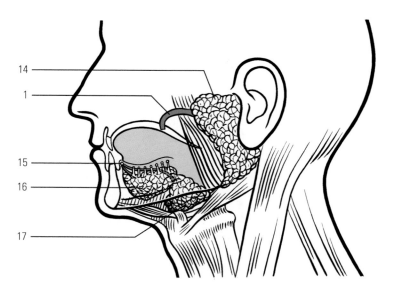

Location of the salivary glands. The parotid duct (red) (1) delivers secretion into the mouth through an opening opposite the second upper molar. The ducts of the submandibular and sublingual glands open into the floor of the mouth below the tongue at the sublingual caruncle (15).

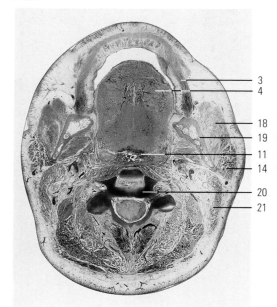

Horizontal section through oral cavity and pharynx at the level of mandibular ramus (19).

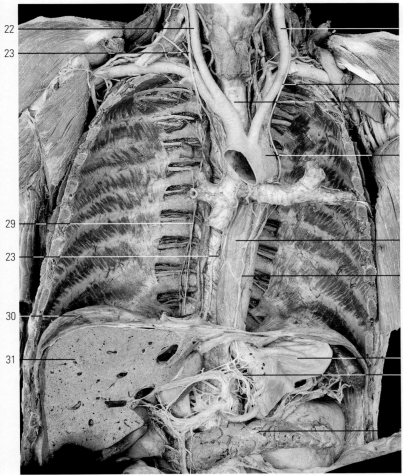

Esophagus with vagus nerves within the thoracic cavity. Lungs and heart have been removed. Vagus nerves join the solar plexus.

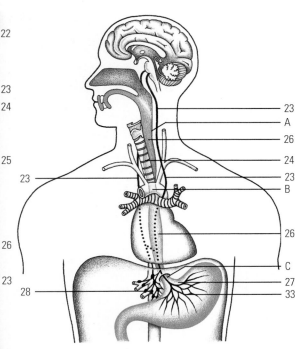

Course of esophagus with vagus nerves which terminate within the solar plexus (right vagus nerve) (28) and the gastric plexus (33) (left vagus nerve).
Narrowings of esophagus:
A = at the beginning of the esophagus, posterior to the larynx
B = at the level of aortic arch
C = at the esophageal hiatus of diaphragm

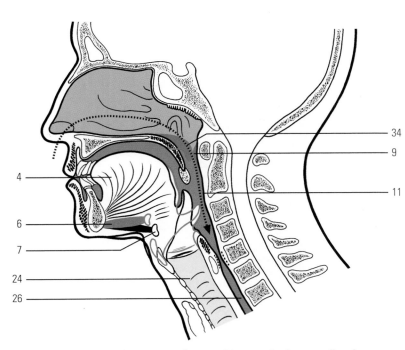

Positional changes of tongue, palate and larynx during swallowing.

Swallowing occurs in 3 phases:
1. The pulling upward of the soft palate with uvula (34) to close off nasal cavity.
2. The upward-forward moving of the larynx and epiglottis to protect the entrance of respiratory passageway.
3. The opening of the entrance to the esophagus ("esophageal mouth").
Artificial nutrition is possible via a catheter introduced into nasal cavity and pharynx into the esophagus (punctured line with arrow).

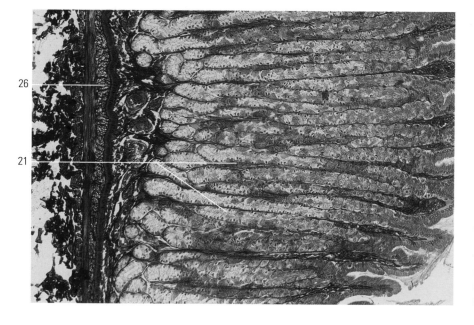

1 **Liver**
2 Proper hepatic artery
3 **Portal vein**
4 Gallbladder (vesica biliaris)
5 Pylorus (stomach) (opening into duodenum)
6 Pancreas
7 **Duodenum**
8 Kidney
9 Ureter
10 Iliopsoas muscle
11 Lung
12 Esophagus
13 Diaphragm
14 End of esophagus (entering cardia part of stomach)
15 Fundus of **stomach**
16 Spleen
17 Pyloric part of stomach (antrum)
18 Abdominal aorta (descending aorta)
19 **Sympathetic trunk** and superior hypogastric plexus (parts of autonomic nervous system)
20 Iliac crest
21 **Mucous membrane of stomach** with numerous, small glands
22 Air within the stomach
23 Stomach (filled with contrasting matter)
24 Duodenal papilla, opening of pancreatic duct and common bile duct into duodenum
25 Spleen
26 Smooth muscle layer of stomach mucous membrane

Abdominal organs in situ. Small and large intestines have been removed, the liver is slightly elevated (anterior view). Note the hilus of the liver (porta hepatis), where the portal vein (3) enters and the common bile duct leaves the liver. The C-shaped duodenum (7) surrounds the pancreas (6) and contacts the left kidney (8). The spleen (16) is located underneath the diaphragm adjacent to the fundus of the stomach (15).

Microscopic section through the mucous membrane of the fundic stomach (light-micrograph, × 30). Note the long fundic glands which reveal two types of cells, the acid-manufacturing parietal cells (red) and the chief cells (blue) which produce digestive enzymes (pepsinogen, etc.).

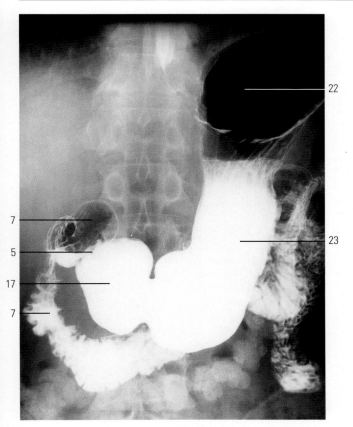

X-ray image of stomach and duodenum after swallowing a barium "meal". The fundic stomach contains a large air bubble (22). The barium has already been transported up to the duodenum (7) and jejunum.

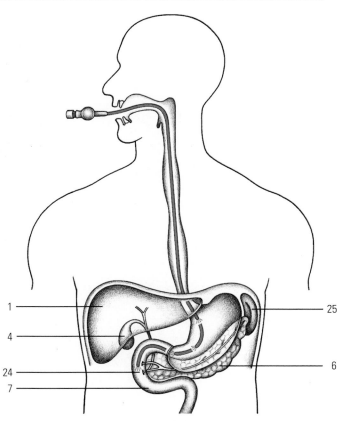

Viewing stomach and duodenum in vivo by an endoscope (red). The endoscope can be forwarded up to duodenal papilla (24), where the common bile duct and the main pancreatic duct deliver their secretions into the duodenum.

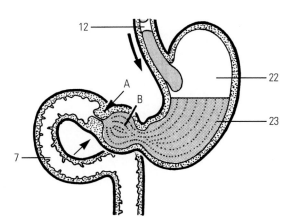

Stomach, filling phase. The pyloric sphincter (A) is closed. The boli, entering the stomach, are added to the previously swallowed food from inside to outside forcing the stomach to widen.

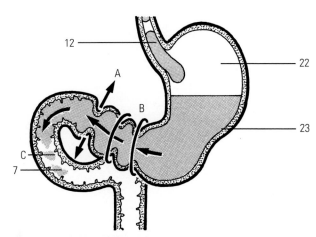

Stomach, peristaltic phase. The pyloric sphincter (A) opens. Peristaltic waves of the pyloric part transport the chymus into the duodenum (C).

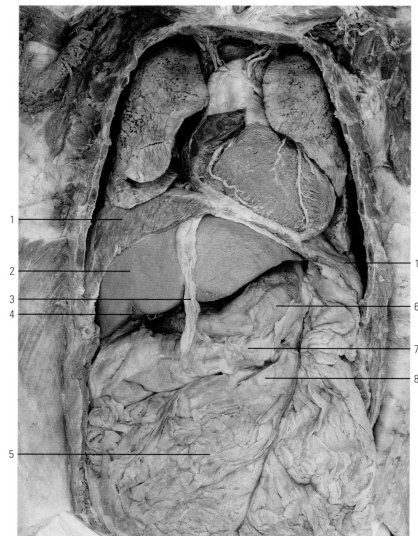

1   Diaphragm
2   **Liver** (hepar)
3   Round and falciform ligament of liver
4   Gallbladder (vesica biliaris)
5   Greater omentum
6   Stomach (ventriculus)
7   Gastrocolic ligament
8   Transverse colon
9   **Lobule of liver** with bile canaliculi (green)
10 Lobule of liver with blood vessels (sinusoids)
11 **Central vein**
12 Branch of portal vein (interlobular vein)
13 Branch of hepatic artery
    (interlobular artery)
14 Bile duct
15 **Portal vein**
16 Proper hepatic artery
17 **Common bile duct**
18 Celiac trunk
19 Splenic artery
20 **Pancreas**
21 Jejunal veins draining blood from small
    intestine via superior mesenteric vein
    into the portal vein
22 Small intestine
23 Caudate lobe of liver
24 Left lobe of liver
25 Quadrate lobe of liver
26 Inferior vena cava
27 Right lobe of liver
28 **Hepatic veins**, draining into inferior
    vena cava
29 Common hepatic bile duct
30 Aorta
31 Spleen
32 Sublobular vein
33 Lung
34 Heart

Liver in situ. Anterior abdominal and thoracic wall have been removed. The liver (2) occupies a great portion of the upper abdominal cavity. The falciform ligament (3) contains the round ligament, a remnant of umbilical vein, which is continuous with the umbilicus at the anterior abdominal wall.

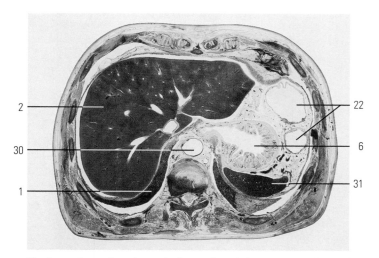

Horizontal section through the upper abdomen at the level of the 12th cervical vertebra (from below).

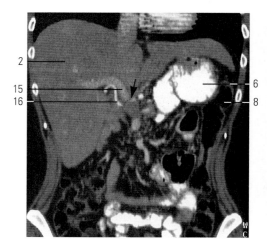

Coronal section through the upper abdominal organs (MR-image). A small tumor is visible (arrow) at the hilum (porta) of liver.

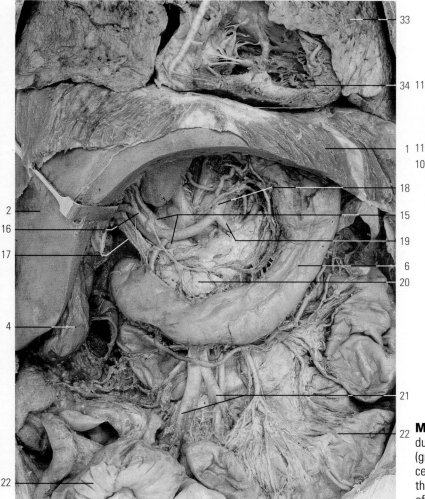

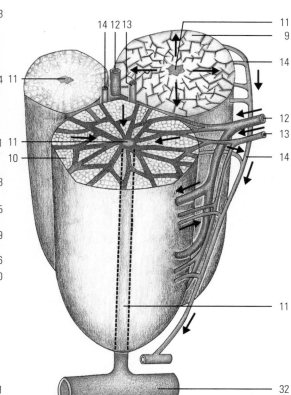

Dissection of portal vein and celiac trunk with its branches at the posterior abdominal wall. A part of the liver (2) has been removed to display the blood vessels entering the hilum of the liver (porta hepatis). The superior mesenteric vein (21) delivers the nutrient enriched venous blood from the gut into the portal vein (15).

Microscopic structure of liver lobules. Bile produced by liver cells is secreted into the bile canaliculi (green in upper right lobule) which conduct a bile in centrifugal direction (arrows) to the larger ducts (14) that run between lobules. In contrast, the mixed blood of the branches of the portal vein and hepatic artery passes the sinusoid in centripetal direction (arrows) into the central vein (11) in the center of the lobule (see anterior lobule).

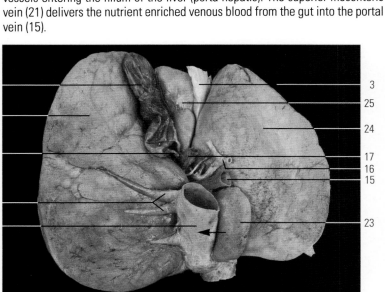

Liver (from below). The hilum (porta hepatis) contains the bile ducts, the portal vein, and the hepatic artery proper. Arrow = inferior vena cava.

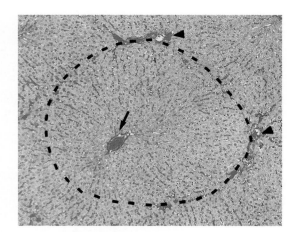

Light micrograph of the liver (×80). Dotted line = lobule with central vein (arrow). Arrowheads = trias of liver (bile ducts, interlobular veins, and arteries).

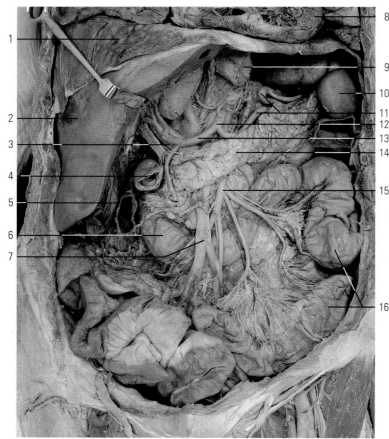

Dissection of intestinal blood vessels (portal system). Part of the liver and stomach has been removed. The superior mesenteric vein joins the splenic vein behind the pancreas (14) to form the portal vein (3) which lies posterior to the common bile duct (29). The spleen (10) is situated underneath the diaphragm near the pancreatic tail (14).

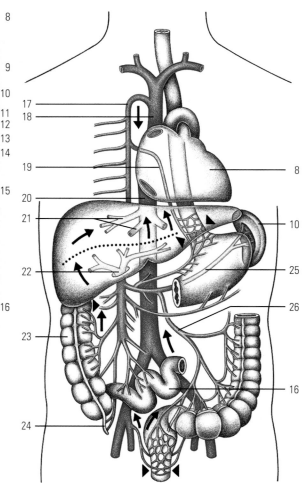

Interrelationship between portal and cava system. The tributaries of the portal vein (22) (violet) come from the stomach, the small and large intestine, the pancreas and the spleen. Portocaval anastomoses between the portal and cava system (arrrowheads) develop at the rectum, the esophagus, and the anterior abdominal wall.

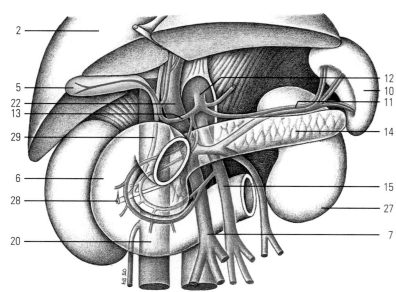

Upper abdominal organs and their blood supply (anterior view); stomach is not shown.

The **portal vein** (3, 22) collects the venous blood from the small and large intestine, spleen, stomach and pancreas, transferring it to the liver. The hepatic veins lie in the superior liver pole and drain the liver blood to the inferior vena cava. Anastomoses exist between the cava and portal venous system in the region of the anal canal, the abdominal portion of esophagus as well as the abdominal wall. Blockade of portal venous circulation (e.g., in case of liver cirrhosis in alcoholics) may result in esophageal varicosis, hemorrhoids and phlebostasis in the abdominal wall (caput medusae).

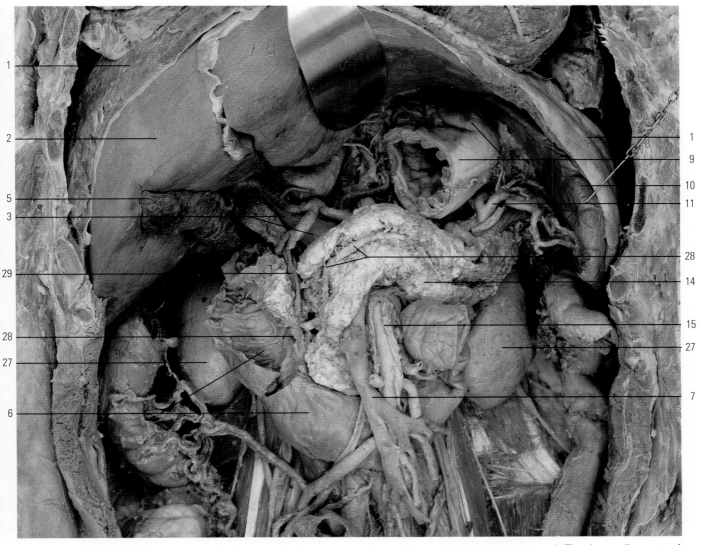

Pancreas, liver, and kidneys in situ. Small intestine, transverse colon, and stomach have been removed. The descending part of duodenum (6) has been opened to display the duodenal papillae, where pancreatic duct (28) and common bile duct (29) open into the duodenum. Blue = portal vein (3).

1	Diaphragm	15	Superior mesenteric artery	28	**Great pancreatic duct**
2	Liver	16	Small intestine		opening into the duodenum
3	**Portal vein**	17	Azygos vein		together with the common bile
4	Pyloric sphincter	18	Superior vena cava		duct at the duodenal papilla
5	Gallbladder (vesica biliaris)	19	Hemiazygos vein	29	**Common bile duct**
6	Duodenum	20	Inferior vena cava		
7	Superior mesenteric vein draining	21	Hepatic veins		
	into portal vein	22	Portal vein entering the liver		
8	Heart		from below		
9	Cardia part of stomach	23	Ascending colon		
10	**Spleen**	24	Vermiform appendix		
11	Splenic artery	25	**Splenic vein** draining into portal vein		
13	Common hepatic artery	26	Inferior mesenteric vein		
14	**Pancreas**	27	**Kidney**		

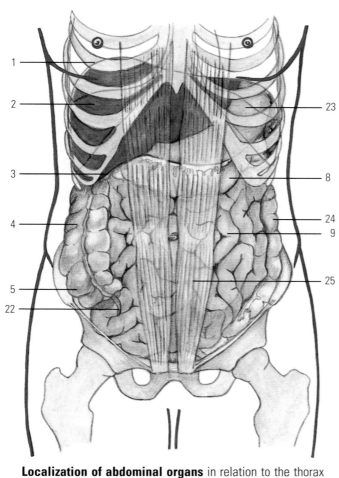

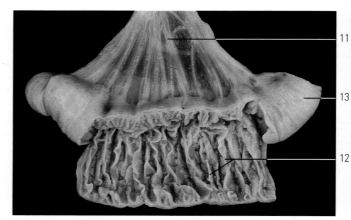

Duodenum, mucous membrane with Kerckring's folds (12).

Localization of abdominal organs in relation to the thorax and rectus abdominis muscle (25). Note that the liver (2), stomach (23), and spleen are located within the thoracic part of the abdominal cavity protected by the lower ribs.

Microscopic section through the small intestine ($\times 12$) showing two folds of Kerckring (12).

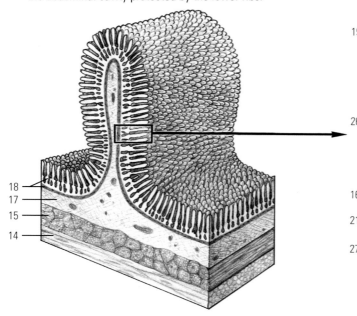

Longitudinal section through the duodenum showing two Kerckring's folds with numerous villi ($\times 12$, Azan stain).
The enlarged picture on the right shows the microscopic structure of the duodenum. Kerckring's fold hosts numerous villi and

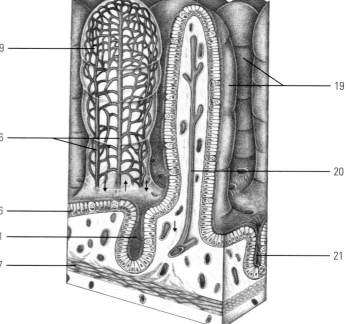

glands. The two villi contain an elaborated network of blood vessels (26) (absorption of amino acids and carbohydrates drained by portal vein to the liver) and a central lymph vessel (20) (right villus) (absorption of lipids, drained into intestinal lymph nodes).

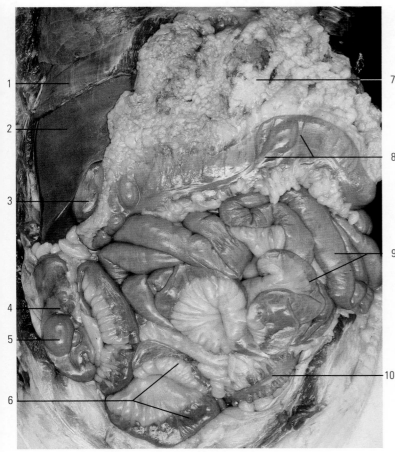

1 Diaphragm
2 Liver
3 Gallbladder (vesica biliaris)
4 **Ascending colon**
5 Cecum
6 Small intestine (ileum)
7 **Greater omentum** fixed to the transverse colon (upward reflected)
8 **Transverse colon**
9 Small intestine (jejunum)
10 **Sigmoid colon**
11 Mesentery with blood vessels and nerves
12 **Kerckring's folds** (circular plicae)
13 Peritoneum
14 Longitudinal muscle layer of gut
15 Circular muscle layer of gut
16 Epithelial lining with goblet cells
17 Submucosa layer
18 Mucous membrane with finger-like villi and glands, supported by a smooth muscle layer (muscularis mucosae)
19 Intestinal villi
20 **Central lymph vessel of villus**
21 Lieberkühn's crypt (intestinal gland)
22 Vermiform appendix
23 Stomach
24 **Descending colon**
25 Rectus abdominis muscle
26 Blood vessels of intestinal villus (red = arteries; blue = veins)
27 Smooth muscle layer of intestinal mucous membrane (muscularis mucosae)

Small intestine within the abdominal cavity (anterior view). Transverse colon with greater omentum has been upwardly reflected.

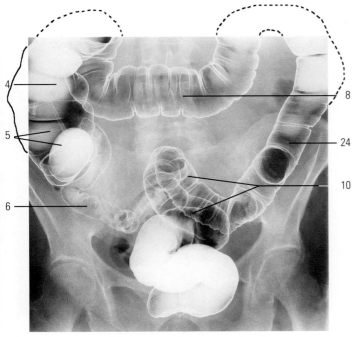

Roentgenogram of the entire colon encircling the small intestine (after an enema with contrasting matter was given).

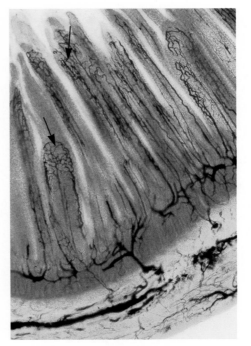

Vasculature of intestinal villi after injection of india ink (light micrograph, ×30). Arrows = capillary network of villi.

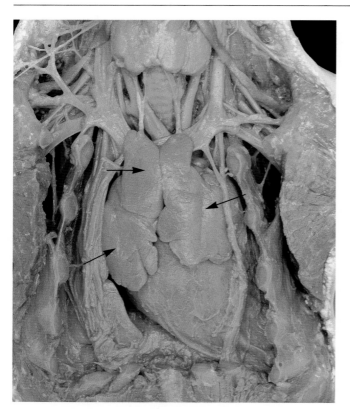

Thymus gland of a newborn situated in the thoracic cavity on top of the heart (arrows).

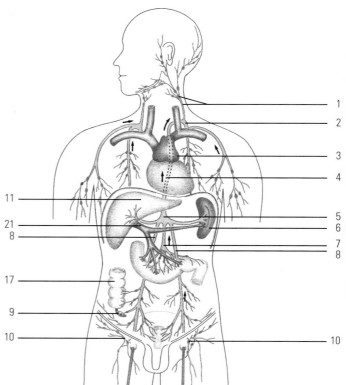

Lymphatic vessels and organs of the body. The numerous lymph nodes (green dots) are always integrated with lymphatic drainage routes.

The body has a remarkable defense capability against foreign bodies or substances not produced naturally in the organism. The defense mechanisms are collectively referred to as immunity or immune response. Foreign substances ("antigens") can reach lymphatic and lymph nodes via the gut or the skin, where they are to be destroyed by antibodies. If antigens reach the blood, they will be eliminated by the spleen. Tumor cells predominantly invade the body via the lymphatics (clinically diagnosed by swelling of regional lymph nodes).

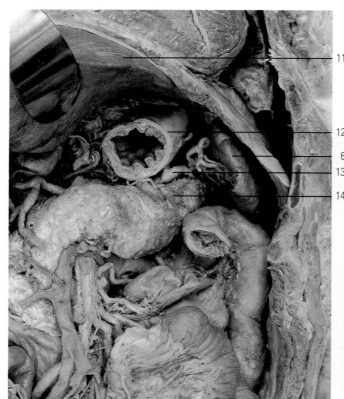

Location of the spleen (6) underneath the diaphragm, between cardia (12), pancreatic tail (14) and left colon flexure.

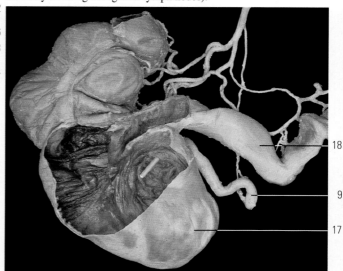

Cecum with vermiform appendix (isolated). Probe = opening of appendix into cecum. Note the ileocecal valve where the ileum opens into cecum.

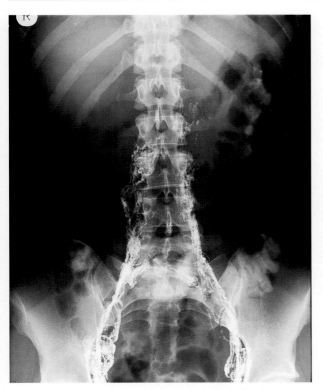

Lymphangiogram of iliacal, sacral, and lumbar lymphatics (30-year-old female); lymph drainage of legs and pelvis is shown.

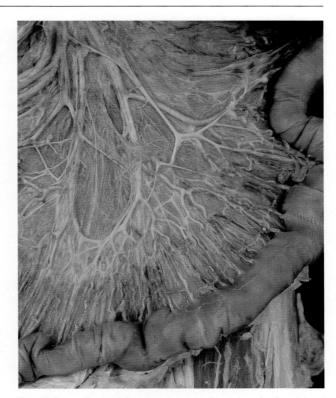

Small intestine with mesentery, where lymphatics, blood vessels, and nerves are located.

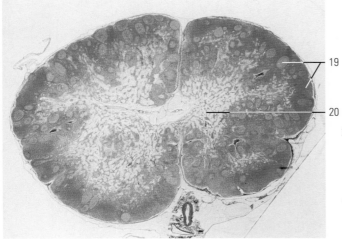

Light micrograph of a lymph node (× 6).

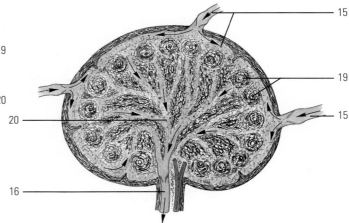

Drainage routes through a lymph node (schematic drawing). Lymph fluid (yellow) enters the node from the periphery (15), passes the cortical and medullary sinus, and exits it at the hilum (16).

1 Jugular lymph trunk and cervical lymph nodes
2 Thoracic duct opening into the left subclavian vein
3 **Thymus** in the adult (replaced by fatty tissue)
4 **Thoracic duct**
5 Cisterna chyli
6 Spleen
7 Intestinal trunk (receives lymph from the intestine)
8 Lumbar trunk (receives lymph from pelvic organs and lower extremity)
9 **Vermiform appendix**
10 Inguinal lymph nodes

11 Liver
12 Cardiac part of stomach
13 Splenic artery
14 Pancreas
15 **Afferent lymphatics** with valves operning into the lymph sinus
16 **Efferent lymphatic** leaving the node at its hilum
17 Cecum
18 Small intestine (ileum)
19 Cortex of **lymph node** containing numerous lymph nodules
20 Medulla with medullary sinus
21 Portal vein

1 Diaphragm
2 Inferior vena cava
3 Renal artery
4 **Kidney** (ren)
5 Renal vein
6 Ureter
7 Psoas major muscle
8 Common iliac artery and vein
9 **Recto-uterine pouch** of Douglas
10 **Uterus**
11 Round ligament of uterus
12 Vesico-uterine pouch
13 Peritoneum (cut)
14 **Urinary bladder**
15 Abdominal part of esophagus
16 **Aorta**
17 Superior mesenteric artery
18 Iliac crest
19 Sigmoid colon
20 Uterine tube and ovary
21 Adrenal gland
22 **Renal calices**
23 **Renal pelvis**
24 Quadratus lumborum muscle
25 Rectum
26 Deferent duct
27 **Urethra** and penis
28 Testis and epididymis
29 Testicular artery and vein
30 Inguinal ligament
31 Lumbar vertebra
32 Liver
33 Spleen
34 Small intestine
35 Pancreas

Retroperitoneal and pelvic cavity in the female. Note the location of the kidneys (4) and the course of the ureters (6). The uterus (10) is situated between colon (19) and urinary bladder (14). The recto-uterine pouch of Douglas (9) represents the deepest point of pelvic cavity.

The right **kidney** is situated approximately half a vertebra lower than the left kidney so the right superior kidney pole touches the 12th rib and the left superior kidney pole touches the 11th rib. Each kidney is enclosed in a tough fascial bag that contains the perirenal fat pad. This bag is open at the middle and the bottom to allow the kidneys to move with the respiratory rhythm. Under pathologic conditions, the kidneys may relocate inferiorly (i.e., floating kidney, pelvic kidney).

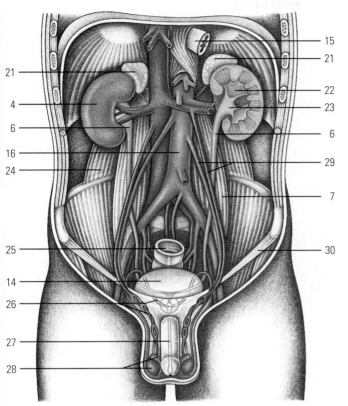

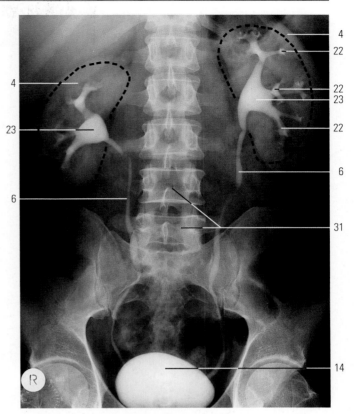

Urinary system in the male. Note the location and structure of the kidneys (4) and ureters (6) and their connection with the bladder (14) and urethra (27) in the male (schematic drawing).

Urogram, showing renal calices and pelvis, ureter (6) and urinary bladder, 20 minutes after infusion of contrasting matter into the blood. Dotted line = area of the kidneys. Note the differences between the form of the right and left renal pelvis and calices.

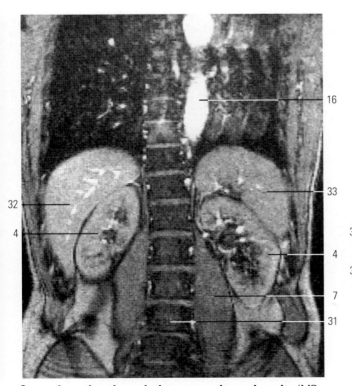

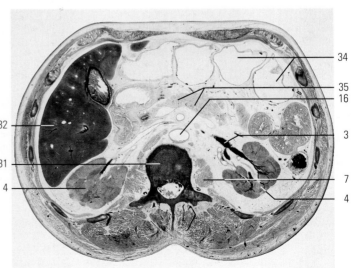

Coronal section through the retroperitoneal cavity (MR-image). Note the convergence of the two kidney axes. Liver (32) and spleen (33) lie in the neighborhood of the kidneys.

Cross-section through the human trunk at the level of the 2nd lumbar vertebra (from below). Note the site of the kidneys (4).

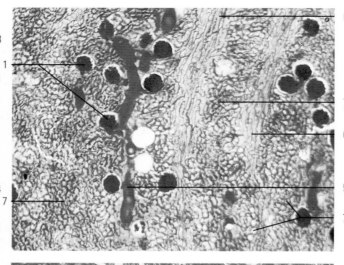

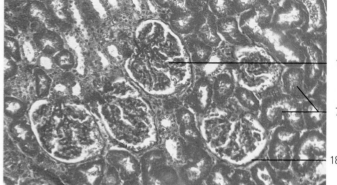

Corrosion cast of glomeruli and related blood vessels of renal cortex (scanning electron micrograph).

Light micrographs of renal cortex revealing the microscopic structure of glomeruli (1) and renal tubuli (7) (above: carmine stain, × 10, below = azan stain, × 64).

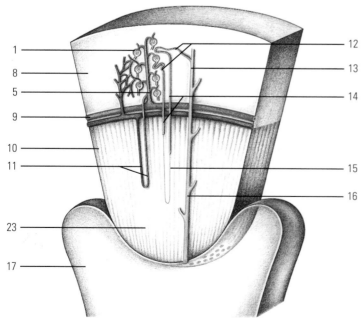

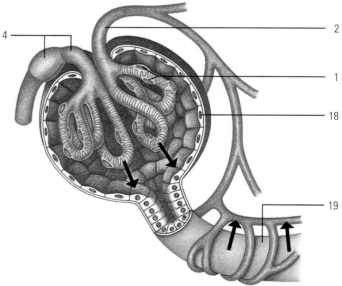

Structure of the kidney (schematic drawing). The cortex contains numerous glomeruli (1) and the convoluted tubuli (12), the medulla contains the loops of Henle (15) and the collecting ducts (16) that open into a renal calyx (17).

Structure of a renal corpuscle consisting of glomerular capillaries (1) and Bowman's capsule (arrows) that passes into the proximal tubule (19) where it is reabsorbed into the surrounding capillaries (arrows).

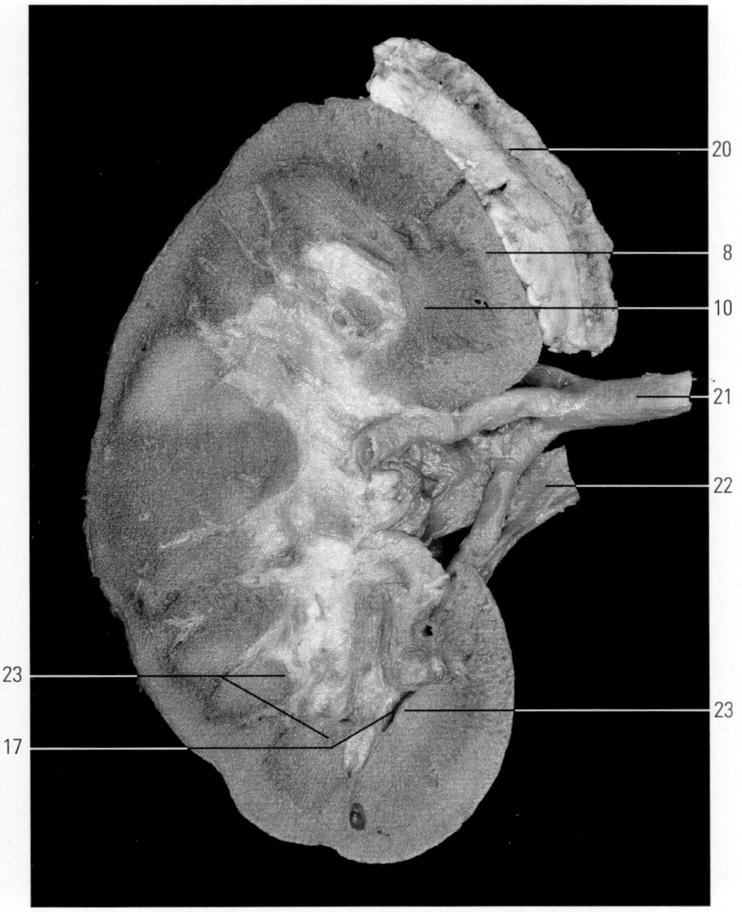

Longitudinal section through kidney and adrenal gland (20). The renal cortex appears dark red since it contains about one mio glomeruli and numerous blood vessels. Note the renal papillae (23) that protrude into the renal calices.

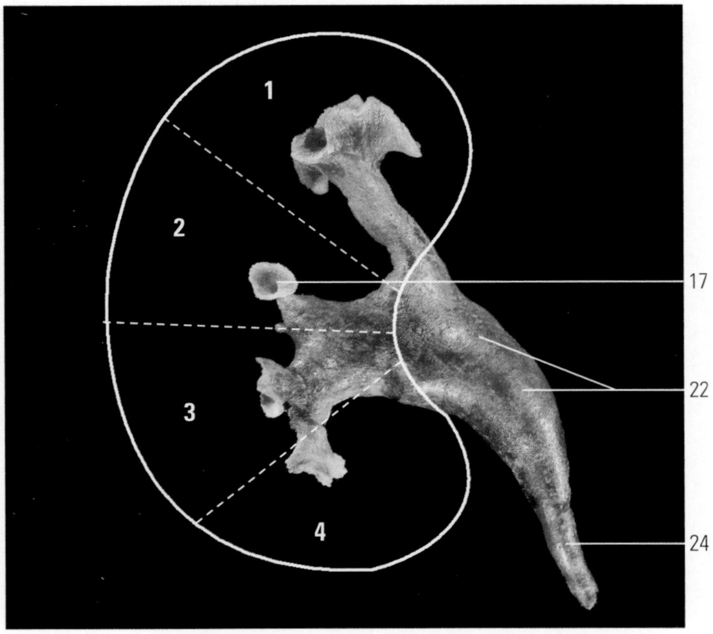

Corrosion cast of renal calices (17) **and pelvis** (22). 1–4 = Areas of anterior renal segments.

1 **Glomerulus** (renal corpuscle)
2 **Efferent arteriole**
3 Capillary network of cortex
4 **Afferent arteriole**
5 Interlobular artery
6 Medullary ray
7 Renal tubules
8 **Cortex**
9 Arcuate artery and vein located at the border of cortex and medulla
10 **Medulla**
11 Blood vessels of medulla (vasa recta)
12 Proximal and distal convoluted tubules
13 Collecting duct
14 Pars recta of proximal and distal tubules
15 **Henle's loop**
16 Collecting duct
17 Minor calyx
18 Bowman's capsule
19 Proximal convoluted tubule
20 Adrenal gland
21 **Renal artery**
22 **Renal pelvis**
23 Renal papilla
24 **Ureter**

Kidneys regulate the water and mineral household of the body, eliminate the metabolic waste products (e.g., urea and ammonia) and thereby regulate the volume, toxicity, and chemical composition of the extracellular fluids. A failure of their excretory function due to disease or injury could cause a dangerous accumulation of nitrogenous waste products in the blood (uremia). Each kidney contains over one million nephrons consisting of a renal corpuscle (glomerulus and Bowman's capsule) and morphologically distinct tubular segments. There is a daily flow of about 1700 l blood (1.2 l/min) through the renal corpuscles, which are situated within the cortex of the kidney. The glomerular capillaries produce about 180 l daily of ultrafiltrate, 99% of which is reabsorbed by the tubular system into the blood. The remaining fluid becomes concentrated in the renal medulla by the loops of Henle and the collecting tubules. Finally, it is passed on into the renal calices. From the renal pelvis via the ureter, the urine reaches the bladder from where it is excreted through the urethra (approximately 1.5 l per day). In the event of kidney failure, the blood can also be filtrated in a dialyzer connected to vessels of the forearm (dialysis therapy).

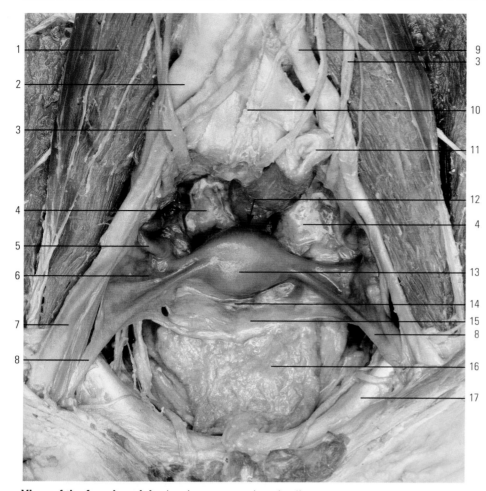

View of the female pelvis showing uterus and uterine ligaments.

Vagina and uterus, normal position
(anteversio-anteflexio)

Vagina and uterus, abnormal position
(retroversio-anteflexio)

Vagina and uterus, reflected
(anteversio-retroflexio)

Vagina and uterus, reflected
(retroversio-retroflexio)

Positional variations of the uterus.
Versio means the tilting of uterus against
vagina; flexio, the tilting of body and cervix
uteri.

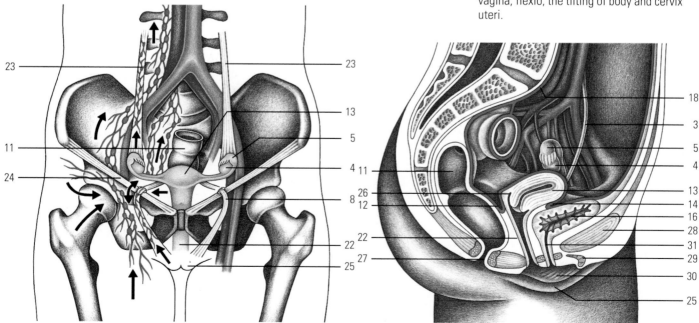

Female genital organs within the pelvic cavity showing the
drainage routes of lymphatics (green) (arrows).

Midsagittal section of the female pelvis. Uterus and ovary are
shown in its normal position. Note the location of the recto-uterine
cavity of Douglas (12).

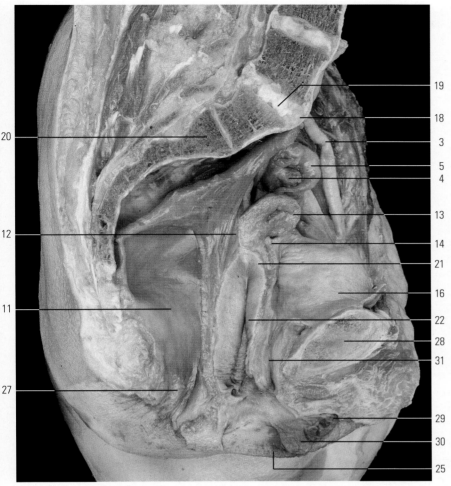

1 Psoas major muscle
2 Common iliac vein
3 Ureter
4 **Ovary**
5 **Uterine tube**
6 Broad ligament (parametrium)
7 External iliac artery
(continuous with femoral artery)
8 Round ligament of uterus (passes
the inguinal canal and ends within
the large lip)
9 Common iliac artery
10 Superior hypogastric plexus
(part of autonomic nervous system)
11 Rectum
12 Recto-uterine pouch
13 **Uterus**
14 Vesico-uterine pouch
15 Peritoneum
16 Bladder (vesica urinaria)
17 Iliac crest
18 Sacral promontorium
19 Intervertebral disc with nucleus
pulposus
20 Sacrum
21 Vaginal portion of cervix of uterus
22 **Vagina**
23 Suspensory ligament of ovary with
lymph vessels
24 Inguinal ligament
25 Large lip (labium majus)
26 Posterior fornix of vagina
27 Anal canal
28 Pubic symphysis
29 Clitoris
30 Small lip (labium minus)
31 **Urethra**

Midsagittal section through the female pelvis (72-year-old female). Uterus (somewhat reduced in size) and ovary in normal position.

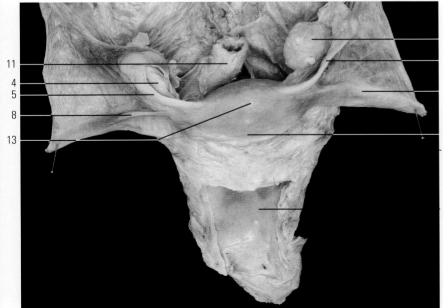

Female genital organs (isolated). Upper wall of vagina has been removed. The left ovary is enlarged because of tumorous proliferation.

Normally, the uterus is flexed at its midpoint and projects anteriorly over the top of the urinary bladder. The cervix (neck) of the uterus opens into the vagina forming the portio vaginalis, which faces the posterior fornix of vagina. There are, however, numerous variations of uterus positions. The pouch of **Douglas** situated at the level of the posterior vaginal fornix is the deepest point of the pelvic cavity. Consequently, injuries (e.g., from attempt at a termination) can cause critical peritonitis. Tumors frequently originate in the **portio vaginalis**. Metastasis is primarily spread via the lymphatic system. The regional lymph nodes of the internal genital organs are situated anteriorly to the sacrum, around the iliacal and ovarian vessels and in the inguinal region.

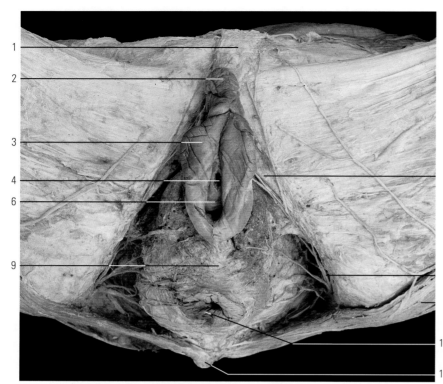

1 Mons pubis
2 **Clitoris**
3 Small lip (labium minus)
4 External orifice of vagina
5 Corpus cavernosum of clitoris
6 Vestibule of vagina
7 Gluteus maximus muscle
8 **Pudendal nerve**
9 Clinical perineum
10 Anus
11 Coccygeal bone
12 Glans of clitoris
13 Adductor longus muscle
14 Gracilis muscle
15 Deep transversus perinei muscle
16 Adductor brevis muscle
17 Obturator nerve
18 **Bulbus vestibuli** with bulbocavernosus muscle
19 Great saphena vein
20 Pubic bone
21 Superficial transversus perinei muscle
22 Levator ani muscle
23 External sphincter ani muscle
24 **Ureter**
25 Rectum
26 Ampulla of uterine tube
27 **Ovary**
28 **Uterine tube**
29 **Uterus**
30 Bladder (vesica urinaria)
31 Vesico-uterine pouch
32 Peritoneum
33 **Recto-uterine pouch of Douglas**
34 Anterior fornix of vagina and vaginal
portion of cervix uteri
35 **Vagina**
36 **Large lip (labium majus)**
37 Hymen
38 Orifice of vagina

Female external genital organs (anterior view). The large labia have been removed. Dissection of the clitoris roots (5) and the nerves (8) innervating the external genital organs and perineal muscles.

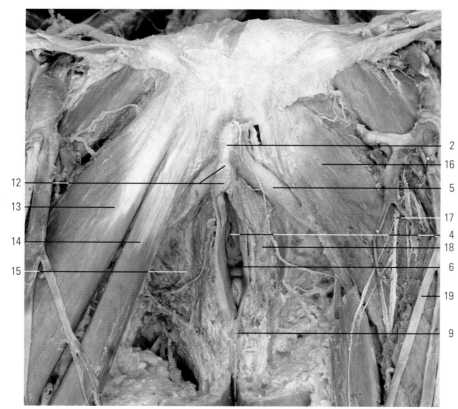

Female external genital organs (anterior view). Large and small labia have been removed to display the vestibule of vagina (6) and the orifice of urethra (4). Dissection of the clitoris (2 and 5).

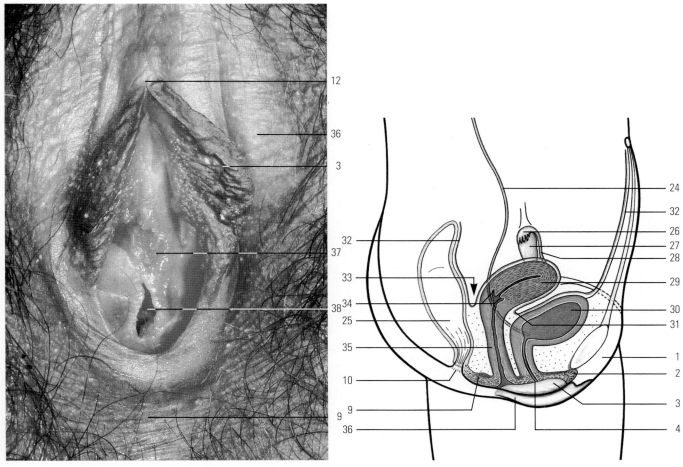

External genital organs of a virgin (anterior view). The small labia (3) are reflected to show the intact hymenal membrane (37).

Midsagittal section of the female pelvis showing the normal position of uterus and vagina in relation to rectum and bladder. Note the location of the Douglas cavity (arrow, 33).

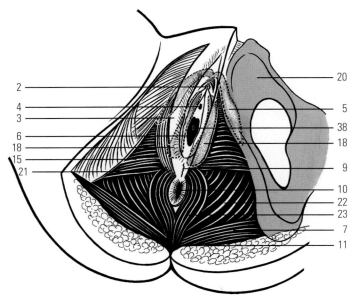

External female genital organs (from below). Form and position of bulbus vestibuli (18) and clitoris (2) both containing erectile tissues are shown (blue).

The vestibule of the vagina (6) is the space between the small lips posterior to the clitoris. It contains the openings of both the urethra and the vagina. The bulb of the vestibule is composed of two elongated bodies of cavernous tissue on either side of the vagina. It is homologous to the corpus spongiosum of the penis. It fills up with blood during arousal. After sexual intercourse (coitus) the blood is again expressed by the surrounding (bulbocavernosus) muscle from the bulb. A number of vestibular glands secrete lubricating fluid into the vestibule. Among the most important are the greater vestibular glands (Bartholini's glands). The clitoris, homologous to the penis, is situated in front of the urethral opening (4) and encircled by the labia minora (3). It consists of two small bodies of erectile tissue surrounded by the ischiocavernosus muscles (5). The uterus neck extends into the posterior end of the vagina (portio vaginalis), forming the vaginal fornix. The posterior fornix is situated at the level of the recto-uterine pouch of Douglas (33), the deepest point of the pelvic cavity.

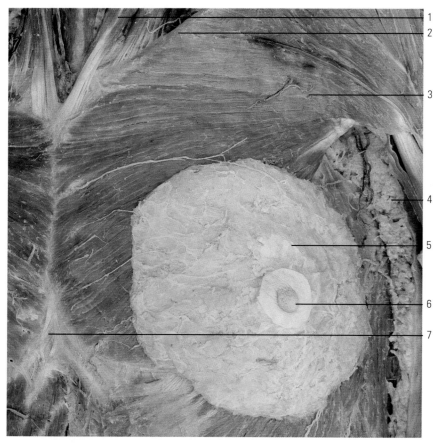

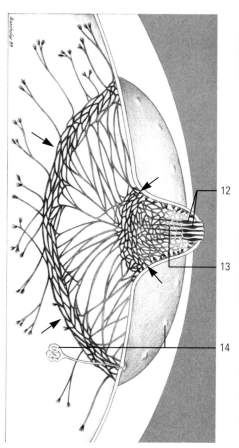

Female mammary gland (left side, anterior view). Part of the glandular tissue is replaced by fatty tissue. Areola with nipple is shown in its normal position.

Sphincter muscles around the nipple and glandular ducts (after Dabelow). The nipple is rectile, thus promoting the release of milk.

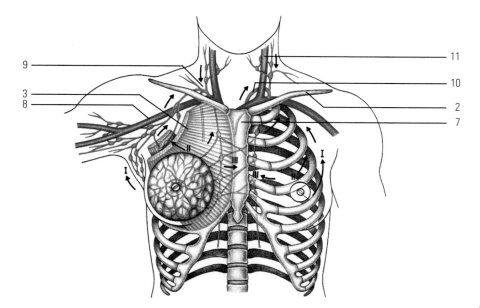

Drainage routes of lymphatics from the mammary gland (arrows). I = main route through axillary lymph vessels; II = intermuscular route between pectoralis major and minor muscles towards intra- and supraclavicular lymph nodes; III = parasternal routes towards the anterior mediastinum.

1 Sternocleidomastoid muscle
2 Clavicula
3 Pectoralis major muscle
4 Fatty tissue of axillary groove
5 **Mammary gland**
6 **Nipple (papilla mammae)**
7 Sternum
8 Axillary vein
9 Right lymphatic duct
10 Thoracic duct
11 Internal jugular vein
12 Lactiferous sinus
13 **Lactiferous ducts**
14 Areolar glands of Montgomery

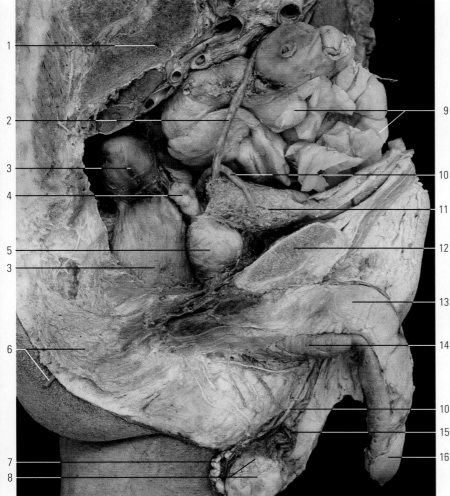

1 Sacrum
2 **Ureter**
3 Rectum
4 Seminal vesicle
5 **Prostate gland**
6 External anal sphincter and anus (probe)
7 Epididymal duct
8 Testis and epididymis
9 Small intestine
10 **Deferent duct** (vas deferens)
11 Bladder (vesica urinaria)
12 Pubic bone
13 Cavernous body of penis
   (corpus cavernosum penis)
14 Cavernous body surrounding the urethra
   (corpus spongiosum penis)
15 Pampiniform plexus
   (drains into testicular vein)
16 Glans of penis
17 Opening of ureter into bladder
18 Urethra (prostate portion)
19 **Urethra** (penile portion)
20 Bulbourethral gland of Cowper
21 Fossa navicularis of penis

Male genital organs (lateral view). Dissection of the bladder (11), prostate gland (5), and seminal vesicle (4) within the pelvic cavity.

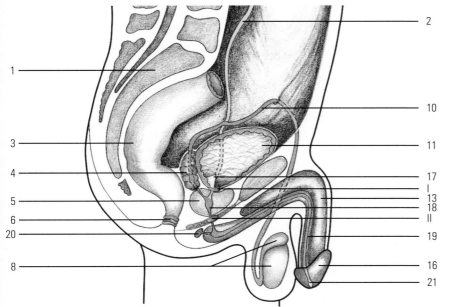

Location of male genital organs. I = smooth muscle sphincter (not voluntary); II = striated muscle sphincter (voluntary).

The **ductus deferens** (10) originates in the epididymis, leaves the scrotum as a part of the spermatic cord and passes through the inguinal canal to enter the abdominal cavity where it crosses over the top of the ureter (2). At the posterior surface of the bladder, it is joined by the duct of the seminal vesicle (4) to form the ejaculatory duct that passes through the prostate gland (5) and opens into the posterior wall of the prostatic part of urethra (18). In the male, the urethra extends from the bladder to the end of the penis (21), conveying either urine from the bladder or seminal fluid from the testis and epididymis (8). Two **sphincter muscles** close the urethra: an involuntary sphincter at the bladder fundus (part of the bladder muscles) and a voluntary sphincter muscle formed by the deep transverse perineal muscle. The relatively complicated nervous regulation of both muscle systems has to be acquired by the child in the postnatal time period. Bedwetting (enuresis) is a consequence of lacking nervous coordination.

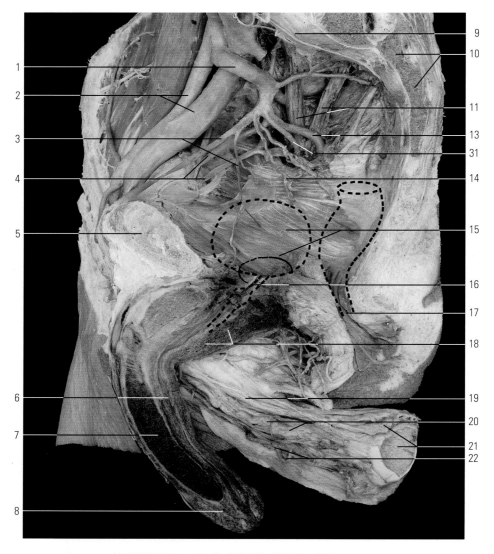

Midsagittal section through the pelvis in the male. Organs of the pelvic cavity have been removed. Dashed line = site of bladder, prostate gland, and rectum.

1 **Internal iliac artery** supplying pelvic organs
2 External iliac artery and vein supplying the leg
3 Superior vesical artery
4 Obturator artery and vein
5 Pubic symphysis
6 **Urethra**
7 Cavernous body of penis
8 Glans of penis
9 Sacral promontorium
10 Sacrum
11 Sacral nerve plexus
12 Superior gluteal artery
13 Inferior gluteal artery
14 Inferior vesical artery
15 Levator ani muscle
16 Prostatic part of urethra
17 Anal canal
18 **Corpus spongiosum penis**
19 Ductus deferens or conducting tube
20 Pampiniform plexus
21 Testis and epididymis
22 Testicular artery
23 Spermatic cord
24 **Urinary bladder**
25 **Ureter**
26 **Seminal vesicle**
27 **Prostate gland**
28 Iliac crest
29 Intestine
30 Bulbo-urethral gland of Cowper
31 Internal pudendal artery
32 Ischiocavernosus muscle
33 Deep transverse perinei muscle
34 Right half of bulbocavernosus muscle

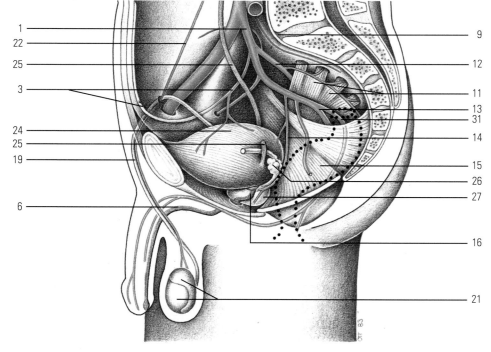

Arteries of bladder and genital organs in the male. Dotted line = location of rectum and anal canal. The two sphincter muscles of the urethra at the prostate gland are indicated red.

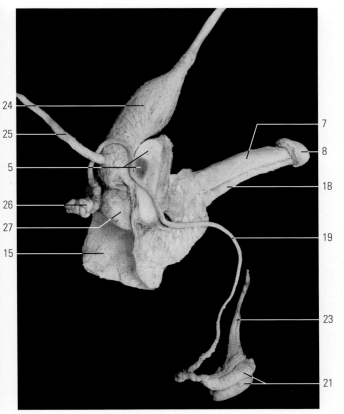

Male genital organs (isolated = lateral view). Penis erect. Note the course of the conducting tube (vas deferens) (19).

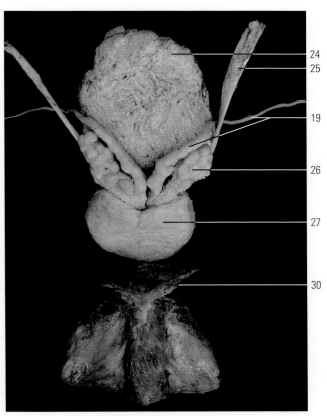

Posterior view of urinary bladder (24), accessory glands and conducting tubes (19) of male genital organs (isolated).

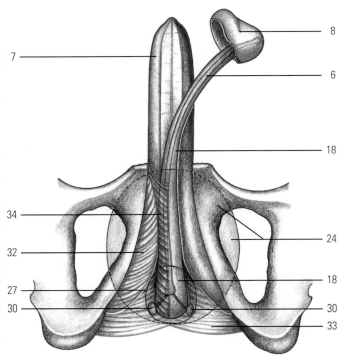

Structure of penis and fixation of corpus cavernosum (7) **at pubic bone** (anterior-inferior view)

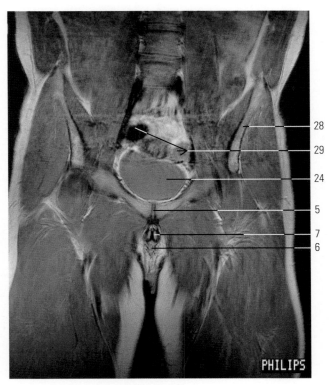

Coronal section of pelvis and thigh at the level of penis root (7) and bladder (24) (MR image).

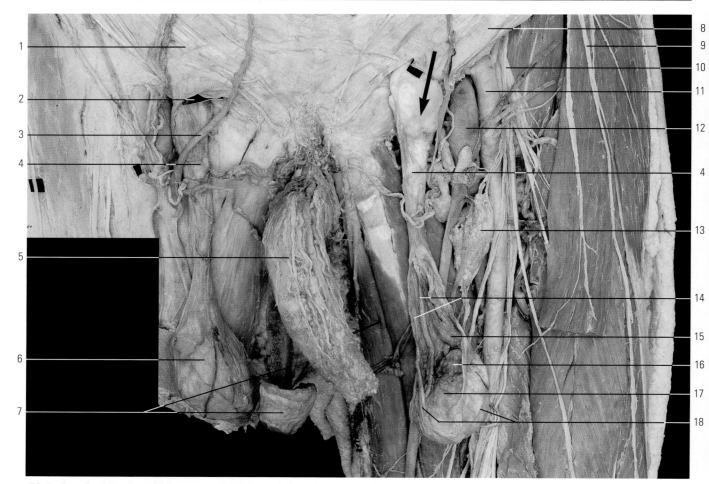

Male inguinal region. Right = superficial layer; left = deeper layers. The corpus cavernosum of penis has been separated from the corpus spongiosum containing the urethra and forming the glans of penis (7). On the left side the spermatic cord (4) has been dissected to show the vas deferens with the testicular artery (14) and the pampiniform plexus (15). In front of the left superficial inguinal ring, a small inguinal hernia (arrow) is recognizable.

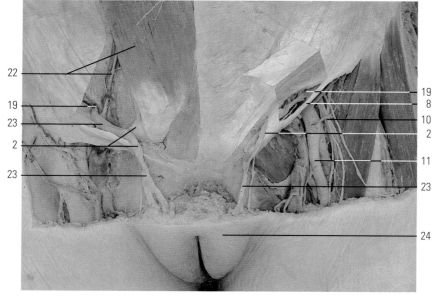

Female inguinal region. The inguinal canal (about 4–5 cm long) has been opened on both sides to display the round ligament of uterus (23).

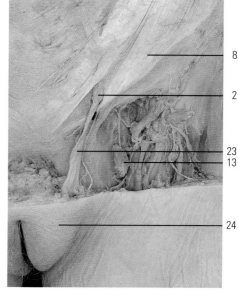

Female inguinal region. Dissection of round ligament of uterus (23).

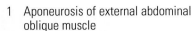
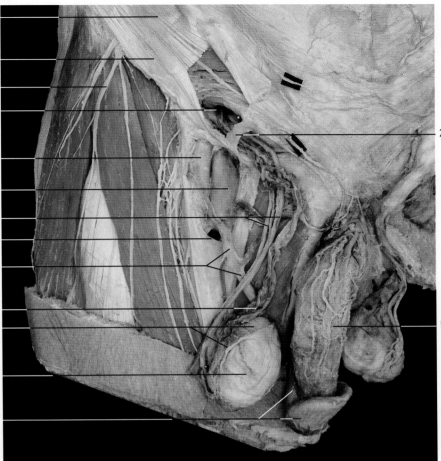

1	Aponeurosis of external abdominal oblique muscle
2	**Superficial inguinal ring**
3	Superficial epigastric artery
4	**Spermatic cord**
5	**Penis**
6	**Testis** with covering sheaths
7	Corpus spongiosum penis and glans penis
8	Inguinal ligament
9	Cutaneus femoris lateralis nerve
10	Femoral nerve
11	Femoral artery
12	Femoral vein
13	Inguinal lymph nodes
14	Ductus deferens and testicular artery
15	Pampiniform plexus (continuous with testicular vein)
16	**Epididymis**
17	Testis with tunica vaginalis
18	Internal spermatic fascia
19	**Deep inguinal ring**
20	Saphenous opening
21	Great saphenous vein
22	Rectus abdominis muscle
23	**Round ligament of uterus**
24	Large lip (labium majus)
25	Urethra at seminal colliculus and prostate gland
26	**Urethra** (penile part)
27	Ureter
28	**Ductus** or **vas deferens**
29	Trigone of bladder, site of openings of both ureters
30	Vaginal process, periorchium, and epiorchium (peritoneal sheath of testis)
31	Cremaster muscle

Male inguinal region. The inguinal canal has been fenestrated to show the vas deferens and the testicular vessels (14). The spermatic cord has been dissected. The testis is still covered by its tunica vaginalis (17) that derived from the peritoneum.

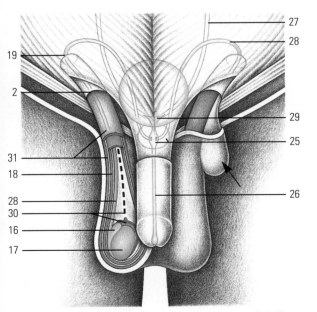

Inguinal canal and sheaths of testis. A small indirect inguinal hernia is shown on the left side (arrow).

Inguinal hernia are three times more common in men than women. Inguinal hernia utilizes either the inguinal canal (indirect acquired and congenital or lateral herniae) or penetrate the abdominal wall directly (direct or medial inguinal herniae). The hernias may contain loops of small intestine and thus cause critical incarceration.

The **covering layers of the testis** are considered continuations of the different layers of the abdominal wall. The cremaster muscle is an extension of the internal oblique abdominal muscle and the internal spermatic fascia is an extension of the fascia transversalis. The peritoneum forms a pouch-like sac (processus vaginalis) which covers the testis and epididymis, forming the epi- and periorchium. The process itself retracts after birth.

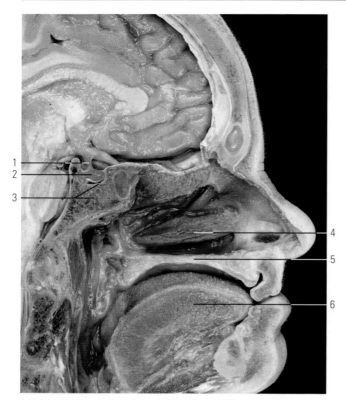

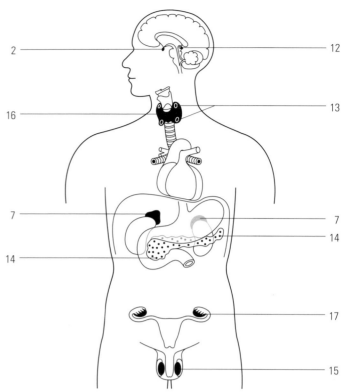

Midsagittal section through the head. The pituitary gland (2) connected to the hypothalamus by the hypophyseal stalk with the infundibulum (1) is located within the sella turcica (3).

Location of endocrine organs in the body. The islets of Langerhans (14) are randomly distributed within the pancreas. The four parathyroid glands (13) lie at the backside of the thyroid gland (16).

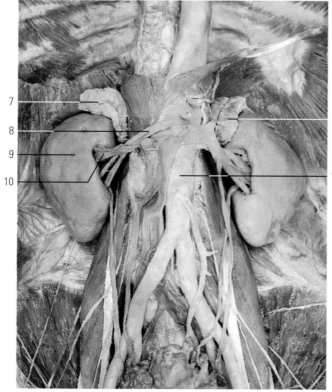

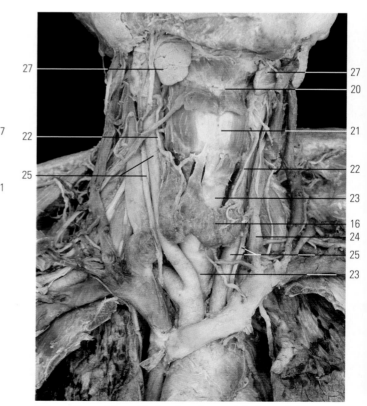

Location of adrenal glands on top of the kidneys underneath the diaphragm.

Dissection of thyroid gland at the neck in front of the trachea (23) (anterior view).

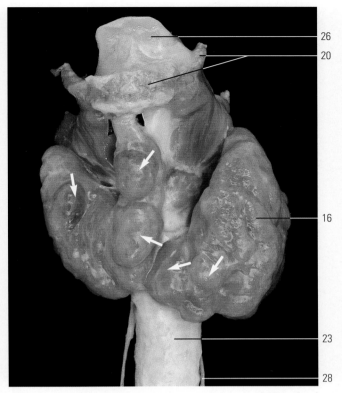

Larynx and thyroid gland (isolated, anterior view). The gland shows several nodes of struma (arrows).

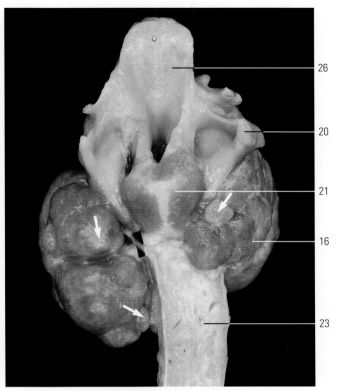

Larynx, trachea and thyroid gland (isolated, posterior view). Esophagus and pharynx removed. Three parathyroid glands (arrows) are visible.

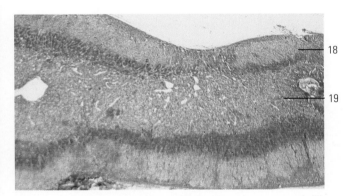

Light micrograph of adrenal gland. Note the structural differences between cortex and medulla.

Endocrine organs – hormones and functions	
Pituitary gland	
anterior pituitary	Gonadotropic, adrenocorticotropic and thyroid-stimulating hormones, prolactin, growth hormone
posterior pituitary	Oxytocin (uterus contraction), antidiuretic hormone
Thyroid gland	Thyroxine (metabolic rate)
Parathyroids	Parathyrin (Ca/P level of blood)
Islets of Langerhans	Insulin, glucagon (blood glucose)
Adrenal gland	
adrenal medulla	Epinephrine (sympathetic effects)
adrenal cortex	Mineralocorticoids, glucocorticoids
Ovary/testis	Female and male sex hormones

1 Stalk of pituitary gland (infundibulum, connection between hypothalamus and pituitary gland)
2 **Pituitary gland** (hypophysis)
3 Body of sphenoid bone
4 Inferior nasal concha
5 Hard palate
6 Tongue
7 Adrenal gland
8 Renal artery
9 **Kidney**
10 Renal vein
11 Abdominal part of aorta
12 **Pineal gland**
13 **Parathyroid glands**
14 Pancreas with islets of Langerhans
15 Testis
16 **Thyroid gland**
17 **Ovary**
18 Cortex of adrenal gland (consisting of 3 layers)
19 Medulla of adrenal gland
20 Hyoid bone
21 Larynx
22 Superior thyroid artery
23 Trachea
24 Internal jugular vein
25 Vagus nerve (n. X) and common carotid artery
26 Epiglottis
27 Submandibular gland
28 Recurrent laryngeal nerve

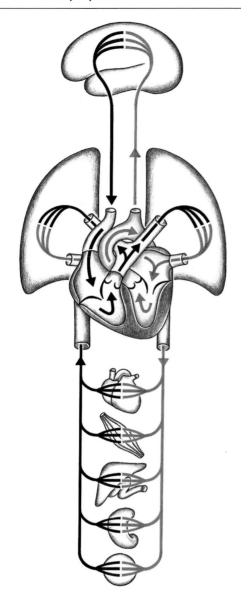

Organization of the cardiovascular system. Arrows indicate the direction of blood flow. Three functionally different portions can be distinguished: 1, brain circulation; 2, lung circulation; and 3, circulation of digestive organs and extremities.

Blood flow expressed as percentage of cardiac output*		
Organ	**At rest**	**During exercises**
Brain	13	4–6
Lungs	100	100
Heart	4–5	3–4
Skeletal muscles	21	80–85
Liver, intestine	24	3–5
Kidneys	20	2–3
Other organs	18	10

* Cardiac output is the volume of blood pumped by one ventricle in one minute (i.e., in a resting adult 5 liters/min, during stress such as exercise 22–35 l/min.).

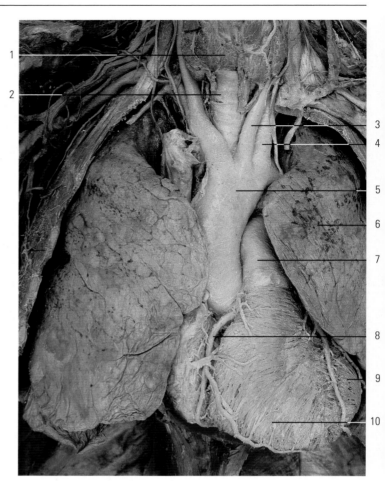

Situs of thoracic organs after removal of anterior thoracic wall. Pericardial sac removed and right coronary artery (8) dissected.

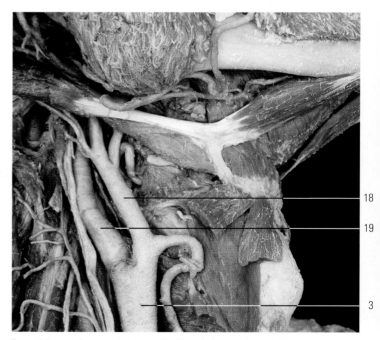

Carotid arteries at the lateral side of the neck are shown. Note the division of the common carotid artery (3) into the internal (19) and external carotid artery (18).

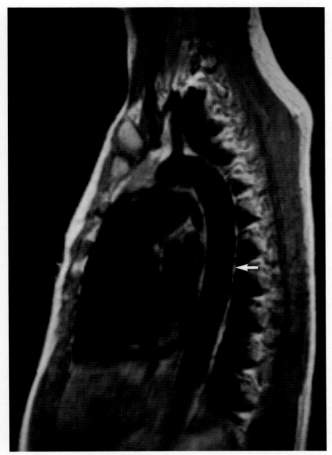

Sagittal section through thoracic cavity showing the heart, the aortic arch, and descending aorta (arrow) (MR image).

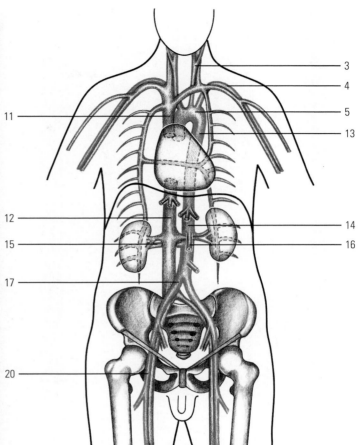

Main blood vessels of the body (schematic drawing). Red = arteries; blue = veins. The superior (11) and inferior (12) vena cava bring the venous blood back to the heart. Within the body, the arterial blood is distributed by the aorta (13, 14) and its branches, the carotid arteries (3) to the head, the subclavian arteries (4) to the arms, the renal arteries (15) to the kidneys, and the femoral arteries (20) to the legs.

The circulatory system can be subdivided into three functional units: 1, the systemic (major) circulation; 2, the pulmonary (minor) circulation; and 3, the cerebral circulation. Arteries carry the blood peripherally from the heart to the organs under relatively high pressure (80 to 120 mmHg), whereas veins return the blood from the organs to the heart under lower pressure (0–20 mmHg). The small arteries (arterioles) represent the main site of peripheral resistance to blood flow, thereby regulating blood pressure. They split into capillaries within the organs or tissues where the exchange of fluid, nutrients and oxygen can take place because of their very thin walls.

Pulmonary circulation: right ventricle of heart→pulmonary arteries→ pulmonary capillaries→pulmonary veins→left atrium of heart.

Systemic circulation: left ventricle of heart→aorta→arteries (e.g., renal artery, intestinal arteries, arteries of limbs, etc.) →capillary network within the organs→veins→inferior vena cava→right atrium of heart.

Cerebral circulation: left ventricle of heart→aorta→carotid arteries→ capillary beds of the head and brain→jugular veins→superior vena cava→right atrium of heart.

1   Thyroid gland
2   Trachea
3   **Common carotid artery**
4   Subclavian artery
5   **Aortic arch**
6   Lung
7   Pulmonary trunk
8   **Right coronary artery**
9   Left ventricle of heart
10 Right ventricle of heart
11 Superior vena cava
12 Inferior vena cava
13 **Thoracic part of aorta**
14 **Abdominal part of aorta**
15 Renal artery
16 Superior mesenteric artery
17 Common iliac artery
18 **External carotid artery**
19 **Internal carotid artery**
20 Femoral artery

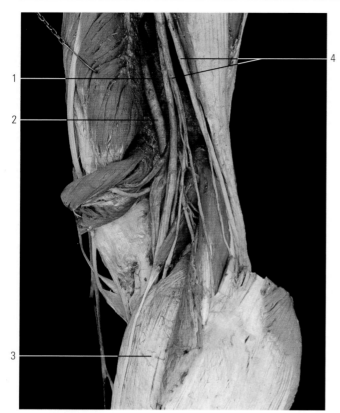

Blood vessels of the popliteal groove (posterior view). Artery, vein, and nerves lie closely together, forming a bundle surrounded by a connective tissue sheath.

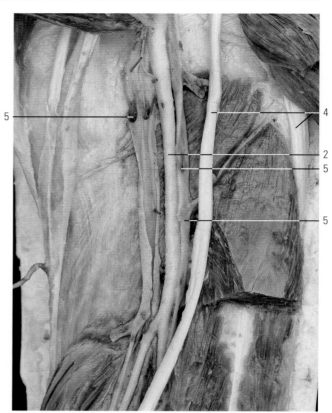

Veins of the leg. Usually two veins accompany the artery (2) and possess well-developed valves (5).

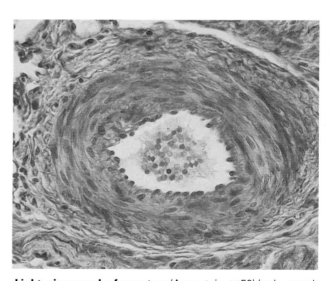

Light micrograph of an artery (Azan-stain, ×50) (red = muscle cells of media; blue = connective tissue of adventitia).

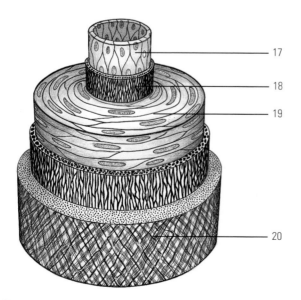

Three-dimensional structure of an artery. The structural differences between the three main layers (intima, media, and adventitia) are recognizable. Red = smooth muscle cells of the media.

1 Popliteal vein
2 **Popliteal artery**
3 Soleus muscle
4 Tibial nerve and common peroneal nerve
5 **Valves of veins**
6 Renal pelvis
7 Superior mesenteric artery
8 **Jejunal arteries**
9 Catheter introduced into the aorta
10 Ureter
11 Lumbar vertebra

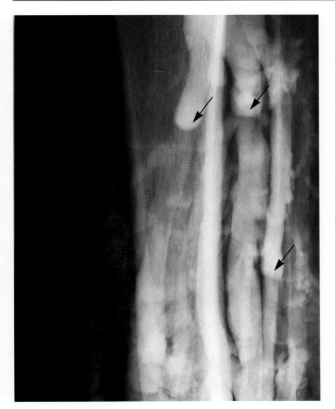

Veins of the leg (X-ray image after injection of contrasting matter). Note the numerous valves (arrows).

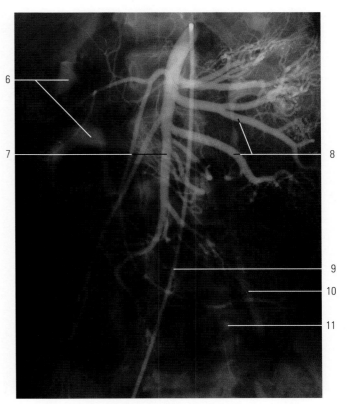

Angiogram of superior mesenteric artery (X-ray image). Contrasting matter has been injected into the artery by a catheter introduced into the abdominal aorta.

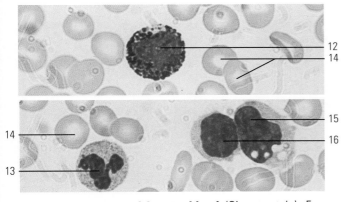

Smear preparation of human blood (Giemsa stain). Four white blood cells are discernible among numerous red cells.

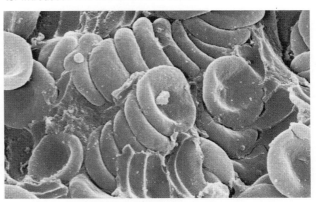

Scanning electron micrograph of red blood cells.

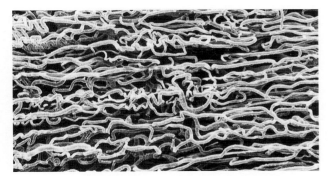

Corrosion cast of capillaries of a skeleton muscle (scanning electron micrograph).

Blood cells
12 White blood cell (eosinophil leukocyte)
13 Polymorphonuclear leukocyte (neutrophil leukocyte)
14 Red blood cells (erythrocytes)
15 Monocyte (macrophage)
16 Lymphocyte

Structure of artery
17 Endothelial lining
18 Internal elastic membrane
19 Smooth muscle layer (tunica media)
20 Adventitial layer (tunica adventitia)

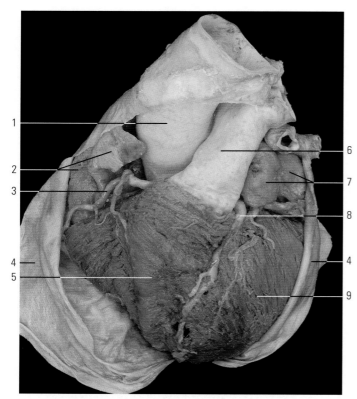

Human heart (anterior view). The pericardial sac has been opened to display the architecture of muscle fibers and the coronary arteries.

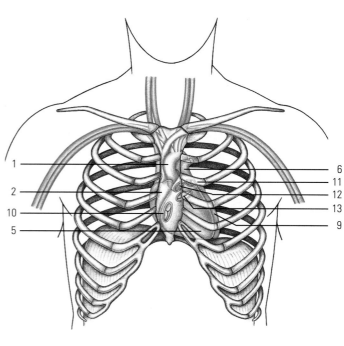

Location of heart and heart valves within the thoracic cavity. The apex of the heart projects at the 5th intercostal space.

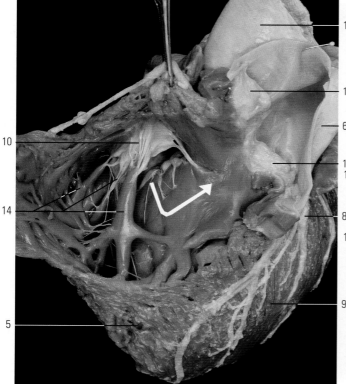

Right ventricle of heart (anterior view).

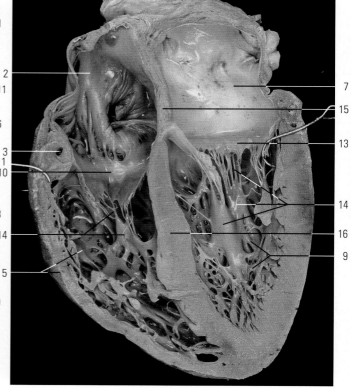

Longitudinal section of the heart showing the four chambers and the tricuspid (right) (10) and bicuspid (left) valves (13).

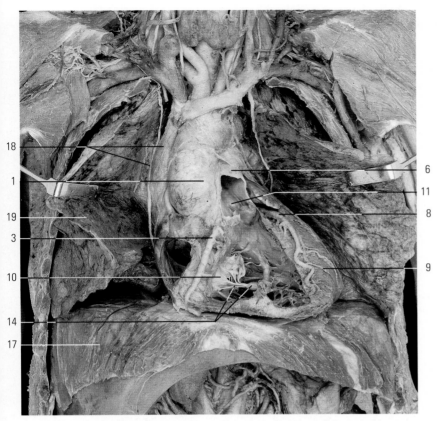

1 Ascending aorta
2 Right atrium of heart
3 **Right coronary artery**
4 Pericardium
5 Right ventricle of heart
6 Pulmonal trunk
7 Left atrium
8 Left coronary artery
9 Left ventricle of heart
10 Right atrioventricular valve (tricuspid)
11 Pulmonary valve (semilunar)
12 Semilunar valve of aorta
13 Mitral valve of aorta (bicuspid)
14 Papillary muscles with chordae tendineae
15 Interatrial septum
16 Interventricular septum
17 Diaphragm
18 Superior vena cava and phrenic nerve
19 Lung (pulmo)

Heart within the thoracic cavity (anterior view). Right ventricle and pulmonary trunk opened to display the valves.

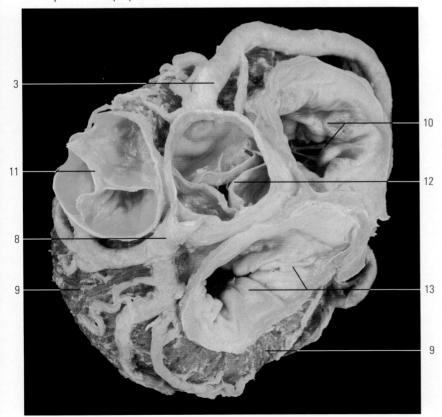

Valves of the heart, as seen from above. The two semilunar valves (11, 12) are on the left, the bi- and tricuspid valves (10, 13) on the right.

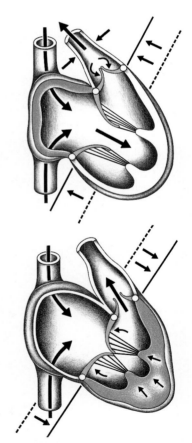

Cardiac cycle. Above = diastole (contraction of the atria); below = systole (contraction of ventricles). Note movements of blood (arrows) and position of valves.

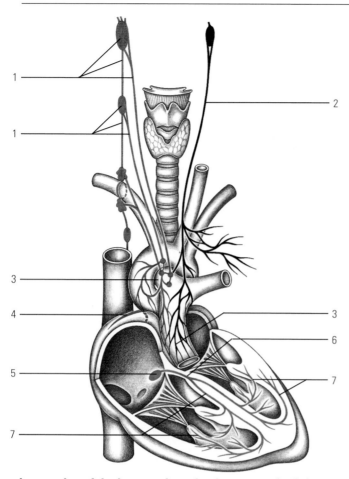

Innervation of the heart and conduction system (red). Green = sympathetic nerves; black = vagus nerve (parasympathetic innervation).

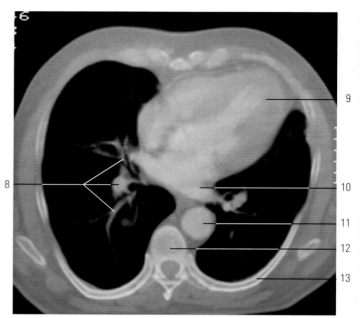

Horizontal section through the chest at the level of heart ventricles (from below) (CT image).

The initiation and conduction of the excitation of the heart muscle is the function of the **conduction system**. Excitation begins at the sinu-atrial node (4) (pacemaker) with a frequency of about 80/min. It spreads throughout the right atrium towards the atrioventricular (AV) node (5), initiating heartbeats with a frequency of 40-50/min. From the AV node, the action potential spreads into the cardiac muscle via the bundle of His (6) and the Purkinje fibers (7). The **coronary arteries** are situated at the level of the heart valves within the atrioventricular sulcus. The right coronary artery predominantly supplies the right ventricle and posterior myocardial wall, the left coronary artery supplies the left ventricle and the anterior myocardial wall. The coronary veins empty into the coronary sinus, which opens into the left atrium.

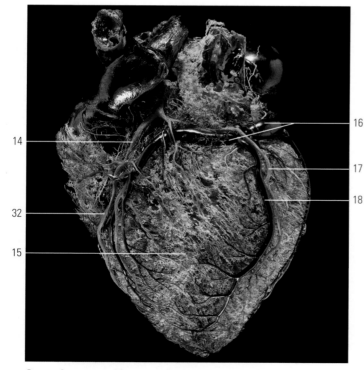

Corrosion cast of heart and coronary vessels.

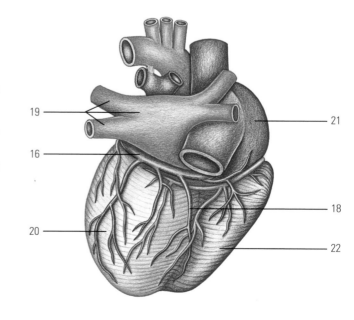

Heart with coronary vessels (posterior view). Red = left heart; blue = right heart.

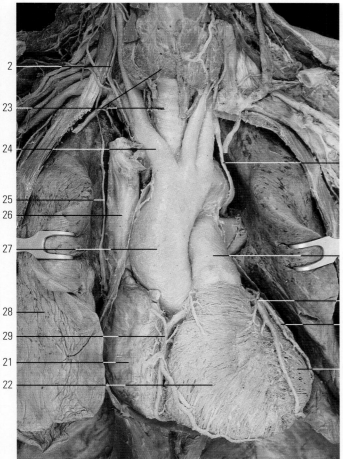

1 Sympathetic trunk, superior cervical ganglion, and superior cardial nerve
2 Vagus nerve
3 Autonomic cardiac plexus
4 **Sinu-atrial (SA) node** (pacemaker)
5 Atrioventricular (AV) node
6 Atrioventricular bundle of His
7 Purkinje fibers
8 Hilus of lung and branches of right pulmonary artery
9 Heart (cor)
10 Left pulmonary vein
11 Thoracic part of aorta
12 Thoracic vertebra
13 Rib (costa)
14 **Left coronary artery**
15 Capillary network of right ventricle
16 Coronary sinus (opening into right atrium)
17 Circumflex branch of left coronary artery
18 Posterior interventricular vein
19 Left pulmonary veins and left atrium
20 Left ventricle
21 Right atrium
22 Right ventricle
23 Trachea and thyroid gland
24 Brachiocephalic trunk
25 Phrenic nerve (innervation of diaphragm)
26 Superior vena cava
27 Ascending aorta
28 Lung (pulmo)
29 **Right coronary artery**
30 Pulmonary trunk
31 Pulmonary valve (cast)
32 Anterior interventricular branches
33 Aortic arch

Heart in situ (anterior view). Dissection of coronary arteries (14, 29) and heart muscle.

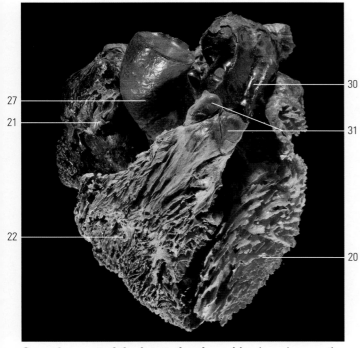

Corrosion cast of the heart chambers. Muscle and connective tissues were completely dissolved.

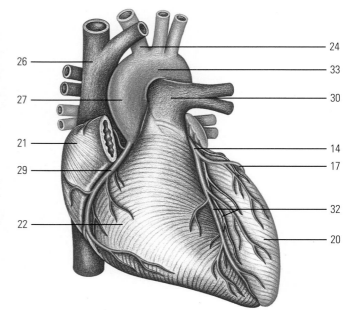

Heart with coronary vessels (anterior view). Blue = right heart; red = left heart.

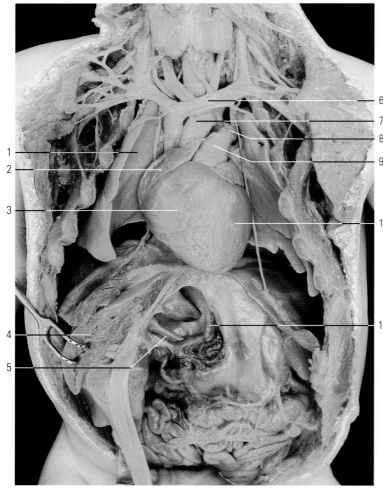

1 Lung (pulmo)
2 Right atrium
3 Right ventricle
4 Liver (hepar)
5 **Portal vein**
6 Left brachiocephalic vein
7 Ascending aorta
8 **Ductus arteriosus of Botalli**
9 Pulmonary trunk
10 Left ventricle
11 **Ductus venosus of Arantius**
12 **Foramen ovale**
   (opening between right and left atrium)
13 Anterior papillary muscle
   and tricuspid valve of right ventricle
14 **Umbilical vein**
15 Umbilical arteries
16 Umbilical cord and placenta
17 Inferior vena cava

● Ductus arteriosus –   to shunt the lung
  (Botalli) (8)   circulation
● Ductus venosus –   to shunt the
  (Arantii) (11)   liver
● Foramen ovale –   to shunt the blood
  (12)   from right to left atrium

Thoracic and abdominal cavity in the fetus (anterior view). Note the two shunts, the Botalli's duct (8) and the venous duct of Arantius (11). Left lobe of liver removed.

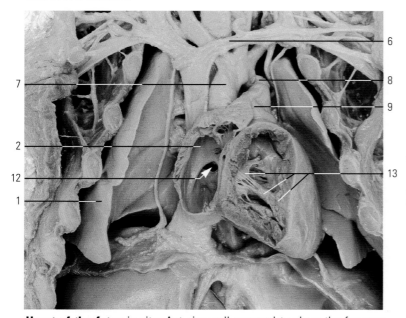

Heart of the fetus in situ. Anterior wall removed to show the foramen ovale (12).

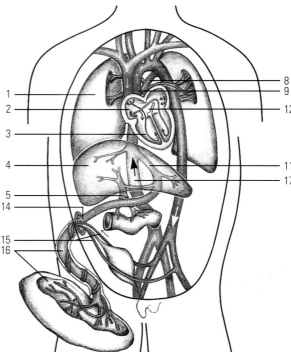

Fetal circulation. Note the two shunts and changes of blood oxygenation occurring in the upper and lower part of the body.

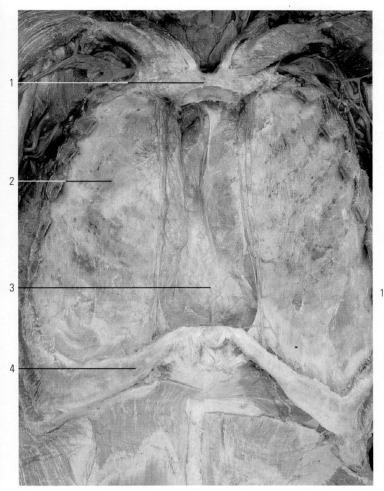

Thoracic cavity with lungs enclosed within the pleural sac (2). The space between the two lungs is called mediastinum containing the heart, esophagus, trachea, aorta, and related structures. The heart is enclosed within the pericardial sac (3).

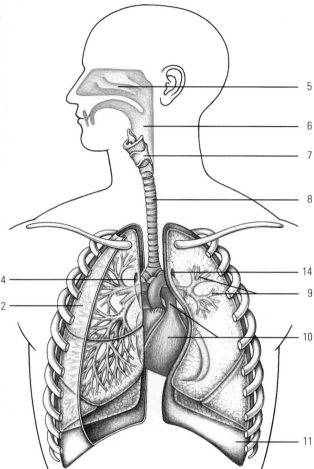

Survey about the respiratory system. The right lung possesses three lobes, the left lung only two. The lungs are enclosed within the pleural sac, consisting of the visceral pleura which covers the lung tissue, and the parietal pleura which is fixed to the thoracic wall. The pleural fluid is provided in the pleural cavity to lubricate the motion of the lungs during respiration.

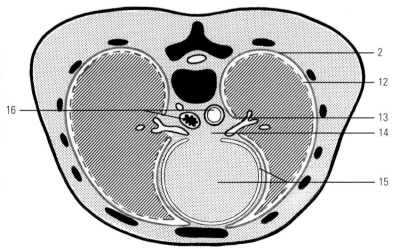

Horizontal section through the thoracic cavity showing the pleural sac (red) (2, 12) and the mediastinum (14).

1 Sternum (cut)
2 **Parietal pleura**
3 Pericardium
4 Costal arch
5 Nasal cavity
6 Throat (pharynx)
7 Larynx
8 **Trachea**
9 Bronchial tree
10 Right ventricle and pulmonary trunk
11 Costodiaphragmatic recess
12 **Pulmonary pleura**
13 Hilum of lung (transition of pulmonary in mediastinal pleura)
14 **Mediastinum**
15 Pericardial cavity and site of heart
16 Aorta and esophagus (situated within the mediastinum)

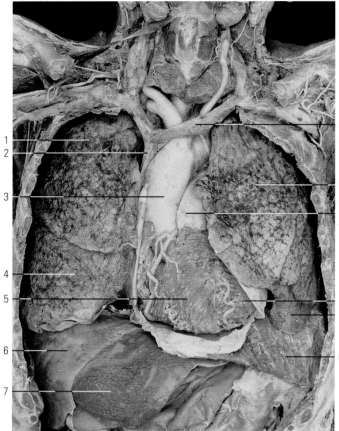

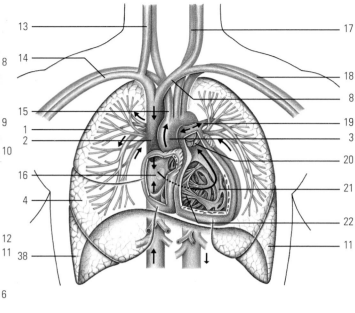

Dissection of heart and lungs in situ (anterior view). Visceral pleura has been removed, the pericardial sac opened. Note the three lobes of the right and the two of the left lung. The black dots on the surface of the lung are caused by pollution of breathed air.

Schematic demonstration of pulmonary circulation. Blue = deoxygenated blood; red = oxygenated blood; arrows = direction of blood flow.

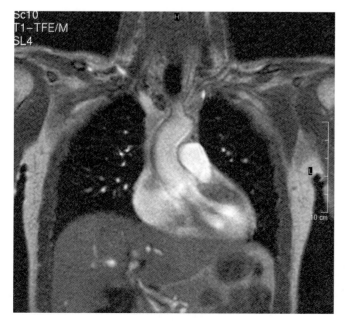

Coronal section through the chest at the level of the anterior mediastinum (MR image).

Pulmonary circulation. The right heart collects the venous blood (inflow from the superior and inferior vena cava and coronary sinus) in the right atrium from where it is transferred into the right ventricle via the right atrioventricular valve. From here, the blood flows through the pulmonary valve into the pulmonary arteries which ramify in the right and left lung. Branches of the pulmonary arteries form the dense capillary networks around the alveolus where the exchange of O_2 and CO_2 takes place. The oxygenated blood then flows back to the heart via the pulmonary veins, which open into the left atrium. Air reaches the lung via the trachea and the two primary bronchi. Inside the lung, the bronchi divide 23 times into two equal parts (principal of dichotomy). Finally, the terminal bronchioles form the alveolar sacs and the alveoli.

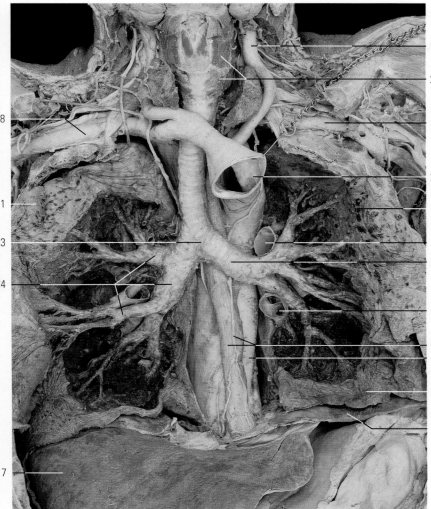

Dissection of trachea and bronchial tree. The aortic arch is slightly elevated to display the esophagus posterior to the trachea.

1 **Upper lobe of right lung**
2 Superior vena cava
3 Ascending aorta
4 **Middle lobe of right lung**
5 Right ventricle of heart
6 Diaphragm
7 Liver
8 Left brachiocephalic vein
9 **Upper lobe of left lung**
10 Pulmonary trunk
11 **Lower lobe of left lung**
12 Left ventricle of heart
13 Internal jugular vein
14 Subclavian vein
15 Brachiocephalic trunk
16 **Right atrium**
17 Common carotid artery
18 Subclavian artery
19 Left pulmonary artery
20 Pulmonary valve (semilunar)
21 **Right ventricle**
22 Right atrioventricular (tricuspid) valve of right ventricle
23 **Bifurcation of trachea**
24 **Bronchial tree** (secondary bronchi)
25 Larynx
26 Aortic arch
27 **Left primary bronchus**
28 Pulmonary veins
29 **Esophagus** and vagus nerves
30 Descending aorta
31 Sternum
32 Pectoralis major muscle
33 Pectoralis minor muscle
34 Humerus
35 Intercostal muscles
36 Artificial space between parietal and pulmonary pleura
37 Vertebral canal with spinal cord
38 **Lower lobe of right lung**

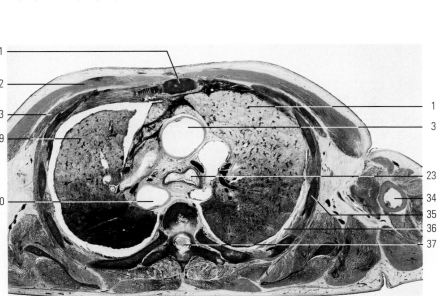

Cross-section of the chest at the level of bifurcation of the trachea (23) (from above).

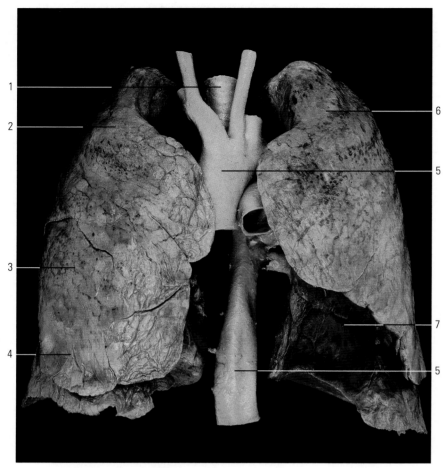

1 Trachea
2 **Upper lobe of right lung**
3 **Middle lobe of right lung**
4 **Lower lobe of right lung**
5 Aorta
6 **Upper lobe of left lung**
7 **Lower lobe of left lung**
8 Branch of pulmonary artery
9 Branch of pulmonary vein
10 Alveolar capillaries
11 Primary bronchus of right lung
12 **Bifurcation of trachea**
   (at the level of 4th thoracic vertebra)
13 Primary bronchus of left lung
14 Sternum
15 Thorax and costal arch
16 Larynx
17 Thyroid gland
18 **Alveoli**
19 Branch of pulmonary vein
   (containing oxygenated blood)
20 Branch of pulmonary artery
   (containing deoxygenated blood)
21 Bronchiole encircled by smooth
   muscle cells and capillaries derived
   from branches of bronchial arteries
22 Alveolar sac
23 Respiratory epithelium with glands
24 Surfactant
25 Epithelial cell of alveolus (type I-cell)
26 Alveolar capillary with red blood cells
27 Epithelial cell of alveolus producing
   surfactant (type II-cell)
28 Transition zone of pharynx and
   esophagus

Lungs with trachea and aorta (isolated) (anterior view). The right lung possesses three, the left only two lobes. Organs of the mediastinum removed.

Thick microscopic section of the lung after injection of red plastic into the pulmonary arteries. Note the elaborated capillary network around the alveoli (10).

Lung structure. The terminal bronchioles form the alveolar sacs containing a great number of alveoli, which are each surrounded by a dense capillary network. The bronchi are held open by small pieces of cartilages and humidified by a mucous membrane containing glands and goblet cells. The cells of the mucous membrane possess numerous kinocilia, which move the mucus (with muck) laryngeally downwards (self-purification of the lung).

Gas exchange takes place through the alveolar membrane and the very thin wall of the adjacent blood capillaries. About 300 million alveoli are responsible for that gas exchange (oxygen absorption, carbon dioxide emission). The total surface of the alveoli area amounts to approximately 140 m^2.

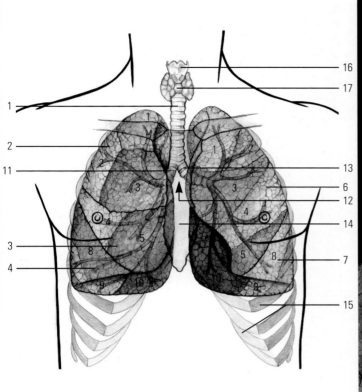

Architecture of the lungs (anterior view). The lobes and segments of the lungs are differently colored. The right lung contains ten, the somewhat smaller left lung only nine segments (Nr. 1–10 in the figure). Bifurcation of trachea (12) is situated at the level of the 4th thoracic vertebra.

Lungs with trachea and primary bronchi (isolated, from behind). Note the different course of the two main bronchi (see the schematic drawing).

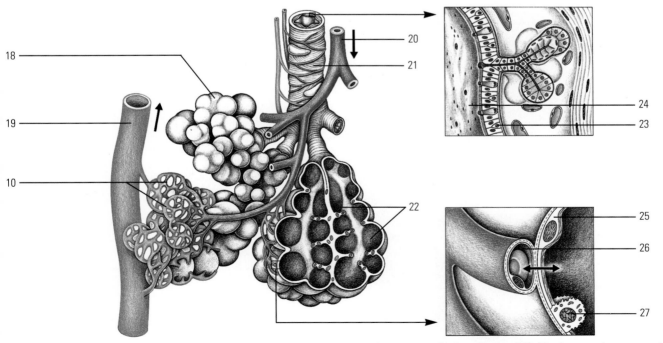

Histologic structure of the lung. The alveoli (18) are surrounded by a dense network of capillaries (10). The lower enlargement shows the structure of the air-blood barrier, the upper enlargement shows the structure of mucous membrane of bronchioli.

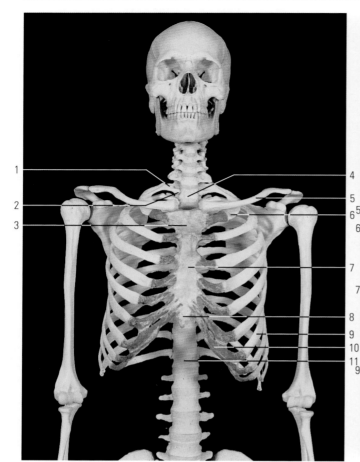

Thorax (anterior view). The anterior portion of ribs consists of cartilage (brown color).

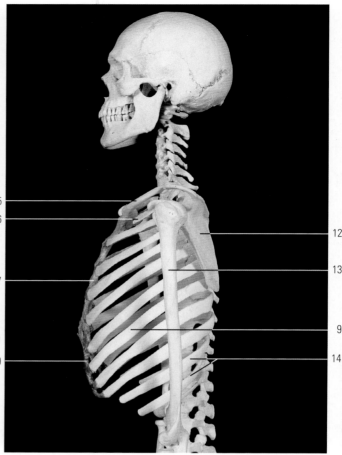

Thorax (lateral view). Note the oblique direction of the ribs in the adult.

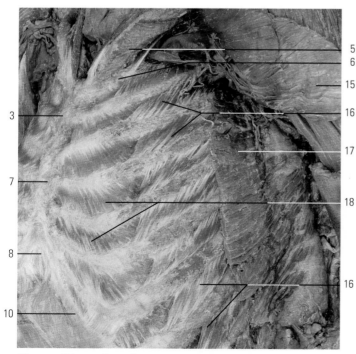

Thorax. Dissection of the intercostal muscles (oblique-lateral view, left side).

The **thorax** consists of 12 pairs of ribs. The seven upper ribs are directly connected to the sternum, the five lower ribs are connected only indirectly to the sternum forming the costal arch excluding the 11th and 12th rib. Each head of rib forms a joint with a respective vertebral body and each costal tuberculum forms a joint with a respective transverse process of the thoracic vertebra. Every pair of joints has a common diagonal axis.

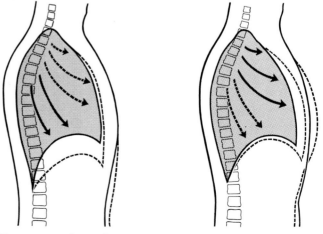

Two types of respiratory mechanisms; left = movement of diaphragm, right = predominant movement of thorax.

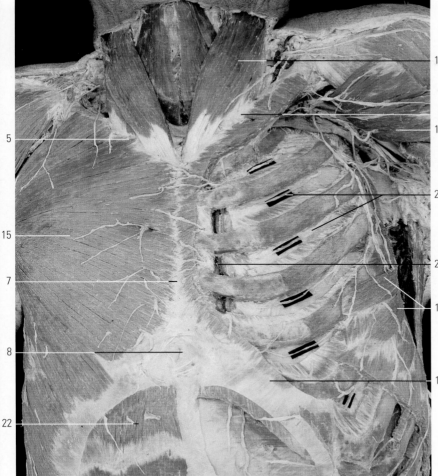

1 **Costotransverse joint**
(joint of the tubercle of a rib)
2 **Joint of the head of a rib**
3 Handle of sternum (manubrium)
4 First thoracic vertebra
5 Clavicle
6 First rib (costa I)
7 Body of sternum
8 Xiphoid process of sternum
9 Seventh rib (costa VII)
10 Costal arch
11 Twelfth thoracic vertebra
12 Shoulder blade (scapula)
13 Humerus
14 Eleventh and twelfth ribs
(not connected with costal arch)
15 Pectoralis major muscle
16 External intercostal muscles
17 Serratus anterior muscle (cut)
18 Internal intercostal muscles
19 Sternocleidomastoid muscle
20 **Intercostal nerves**
(running in the costal groove)
21 Internal thoracic artery
22 Abdominal rectus muscle

Anterior thoracic wall. Dissection of muscles. Right = superficial layer; left = deeper layer. Note: vessels and nerves (20) run underneath the ribs (costal groove).

Respiratory mechanisms: During the process of **thoracic** (sternocostal) **respiration**, the external intercostal muscles pull the ribs upwards (inspiration) so the thorax expands forwards and sideways. The internal intercostal muscles pull the ribs downwards resulting in expiration. During the process of **abdominal** (costophrenic) **respiration**, the diaphragm supported by the lower ribs contracts so the thorax expands downwards, which leads to inspiration.

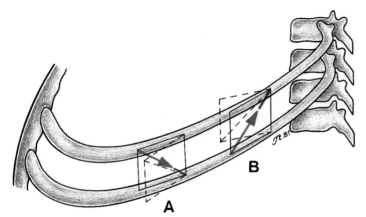

Mode of action of intercostal muscles. A = effect of internal intercostal muscle (expiration); B = effect of external intercostal muscle (inspiration).

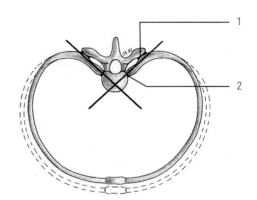

Axis of the two rib joints responsible for rib motions.

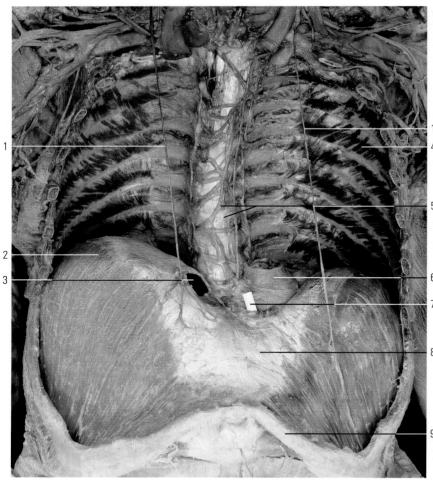

◀ Dissection of the diaphragm (anterior view). The muscle fibers insert in the tendinous centrum (8), the place where the heart is located. The diaphragm is innervated by left and right phrenic nerves (1) deriving from the cervical plexus (C₄).

1 Phrenic nerve (C_4)
2 **Diaphragm**
3 Inferior vena cava
4 Internal intercostalis muscle
5 Vertebral column, thoracic part
6 Aorta
7 Esophagus passing the diaphragm (white probe)
8 **Tendinous centrum of diaphragm**
9 Costal arch
10 Esophageal orifice
11 Lumbar portion of diaphragm
12 Medial and lateral lumbocostal arches
13 Trachea
14 Right ventricle
15 Parietal pleura
16 **Costodiaphragmatic recess**
17 Pulmonary pleura

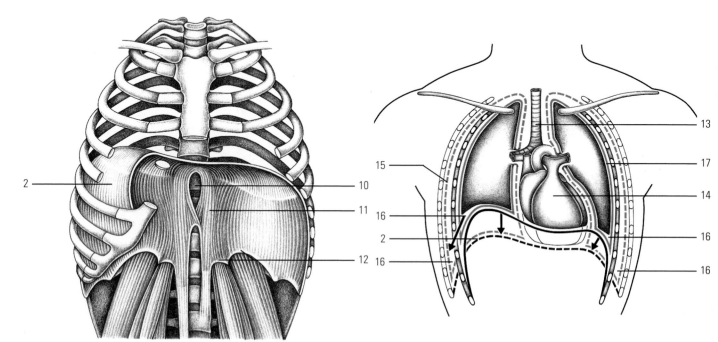

Structure and openings of the diaphragm (schematic drawing). Note the hiatus of esophagus (10).

Mechanism of respiration. Contraction of diaphragm leads to enlargement of thoracic space (inspiration). The costodiaphragmatic recess (16) opens (oblique arrow) and the lungs extend into the enlarged space.

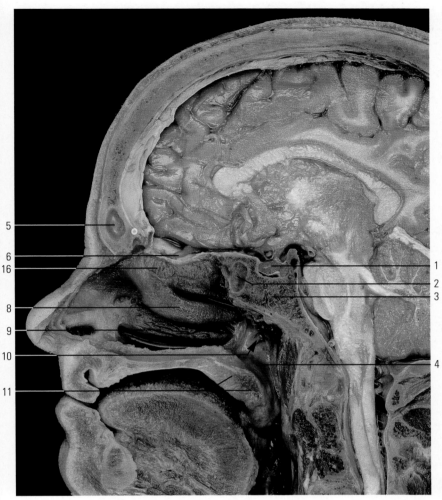

Sagittal section through the head. The upper part of nasal cavity represents the olfactory region, the origin of the olfactory nerves (16).

1 Pituitary gland
2 Sphenoidal sinus
3 Body of sphenoid bone
4 Nasopharynx
5 Frontal sinus
6 Olfactory bulb
7 Olfactory region of nasal cavity
8 Middle nasal concha
9 Inferior nasal concha
10 Auditory tube (eustachian tube)
11 Soft palate with uvula
12 Olfactory tract
13 Olfactory area of temporal lobe
    (brain center for olfactory sensation)
14 **Receptor cells** of olfactory mucous
    membrane
15 Bowman's gland
16 Nonmyelinated axons of receptor cells
    (nerve fiber bundles)
17 Limbic system of brain
    (in connection with olfactory system)

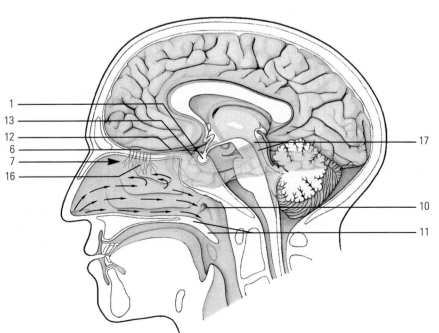

Survey of the olfactory system and its connection with the limbic system of the brain (yellow) (17). Small arrows = course of air in the nasal cavity.

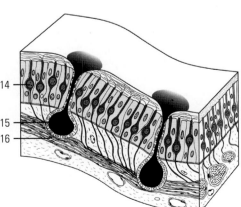

Microscopic structure of olfactory mucous membrane. The olfactory neurons (14) are indicated in red.

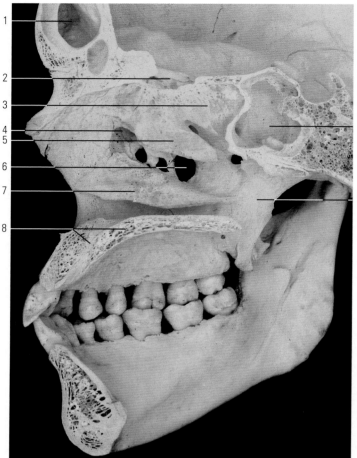

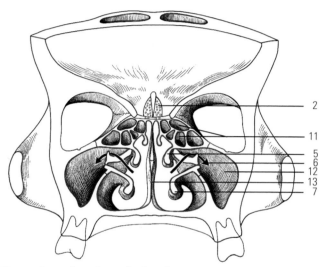

Entrances to paranasal sinus	
● Under superior nasal concha	Ethmoidal air cells
● Under middle nasal concha	Maxillary sinus
	Frontal sinus
● Under inferior nasal concha	Nasolacrimal duct
● Posterior to superior nasal concha	Sphenoidal sinus

Sagittal section through the skull showing the bones of the nasal cavity, the superior (3), middle (5), and inferior concha (7) as the maxillary hiatus (6) (see figure on opposite page).

Coronal section through the skull showing the entrances to the paranasal sinus (arrows). Red = respiratory mucous membranes; blue = olfactory mucous membrane.

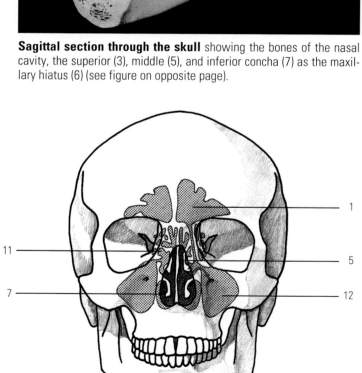

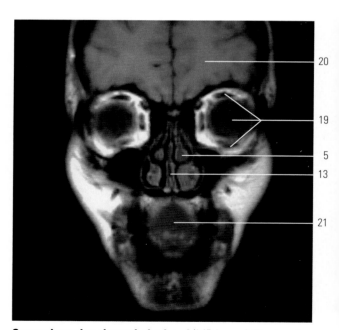

Location of paranasal sinus (1, 11, 12). Red arrow = entrance into the maxillary sinus under the middle nasal concha (5).

Coronal section through the head (MR image). The location of nasal septum (13) and nasal conchae are recognizable.

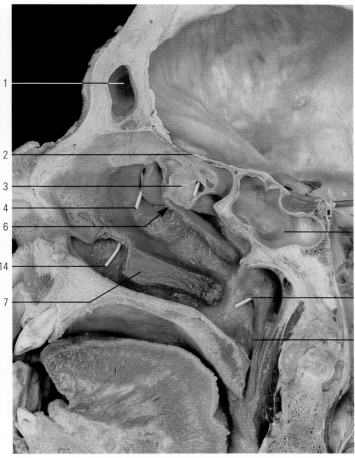

1 **Frontal sinus**
2 Lamina cribrosa
3 **Superior nasal concha**
4 Opening of frontal sinus (probe)
5 **Middle nasal concha**
6 Orifice of maxillary sinus (hiatus maxillaris)
7 **Inferior nasal concha**
8 Hard palate and nasopalatine canal
9 **Sphenoidal sinus**
10 Palatine bone
11 **Ethmoidal sinuses**
12 **Maxillary sinus**
13 Nasal septum
14 Opening of nasolacrimal duct (probe)
15 Opening of auditory tube (probe),
   eustachian tube
16 Nasopharynx
17 Lateral pterygoid muscle
18 Neck of mandible (collum mandibulae)
19 Eyeball and extraocular muscles
20 Brain (frontal lobe)
21 Tongue

Dissection of the nasal cavity. The middle nasal concha has been removed to show the entrance to maxillary sinus (6). The inferior nasal concha has been fenestrated to show the opening of nasolacrimal duct (14). Entrances to paranasal sinus are marked by white probes.

The **paranasal sinuses** are lined with respiratory mucous membranes, which makes them prone to inflammations spreading from the nose (sinusitis). Inflammations can also spread from ethmoidal and sphenoidal sinuses to the meningeal coverings of the brain. Because the maxillary sinus is mostly situated near the roots of the superior molar teeth, inflammations can also spread from roots to sinus.

Horizontal section through the head showing nasal septum (13), connection of nasal cavity to the pharynx (16) and maxillary sinus (12).

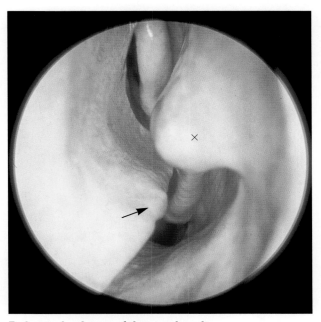

Endoscopic picture of the nasal cavity
✕ = inferior nasal concha; arrow = septum deviation (courtesy of Prof. Rettinger, Ulm).

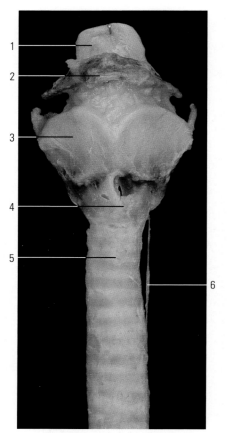

Skeleton of larynx and trachea (anterior view).

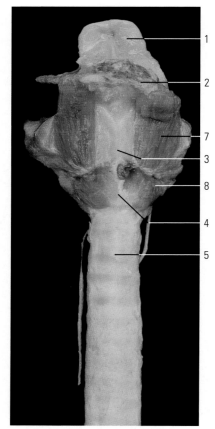

Muscles of larynx (anterior view).

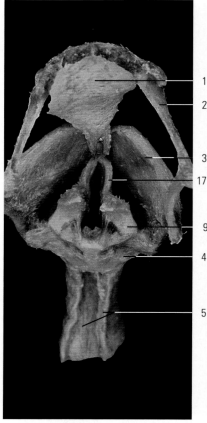

Skeleton of larynx, vocal ligament (17) and epiglottis (1) (from above and behind).

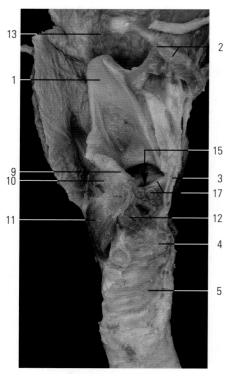

Intrinsic muscles of larynx. Right half of thyroid cartilage removed to display vocalis muscle and vocal cord (17).

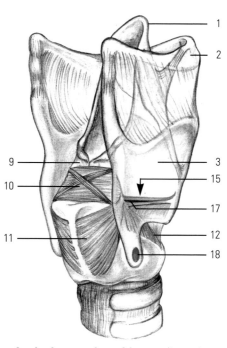

Intrinsic muscles of larynx (lateral-posterior view). Yellow = vocal cord and elastic conus.

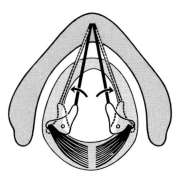

Opening of glottis by contraction of "Posticus".

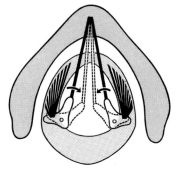

Closure of glottis by contraction of "Lateralis". Note the rotation of arytenoid cartilage.

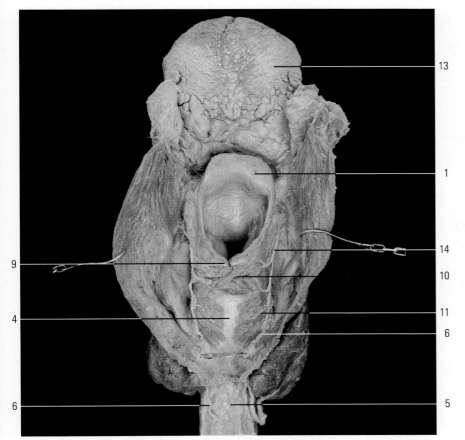

1 **Epiglottis**
2 Hyoid bone
3 **Thyroid cartilage**
4 **Cricoid cartilage**
5 Trachea
6 Recurrent laryngeal nerve
 (branch of vagus nerve)
7 Thyrohyoid muscle
8 Cricothyroid muscle
9 **Arytenoid cartilage**
10 Arytenoid muscle
11 **Posterior cricoarytenoid muscle**
 (opens the rima glottidis)
12 **Lateral cricoarytenoid muscle**
 (closes the rima glottidis)
13 Tongue (lingua)
14 Superior laryngeal nerve
 (branch of vagus nerve)
15 **Rima of glottis**
16 Cervical vertebra
17 **Vocal ligament** and **vocalis muscle**
18 Cricothyroid joint

Larynx and tongue (posterior view). Laryngopharynx has been opened to display intrinsic laryngeal muscles (10, 11) and their innervation (14).

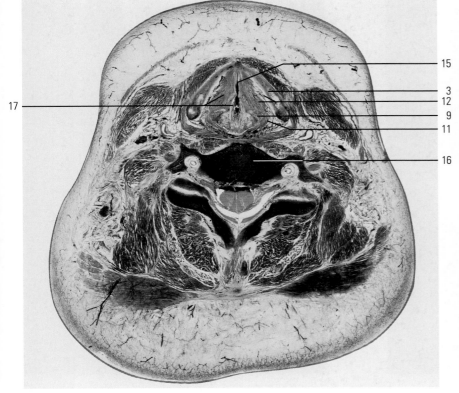

Horizontal section through the neck at the level of vocal cords (17).

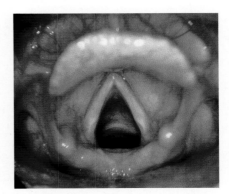

Laryngoscopic picture. Rima of glottis is opened.

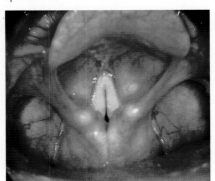

Rima of glottis is closed.

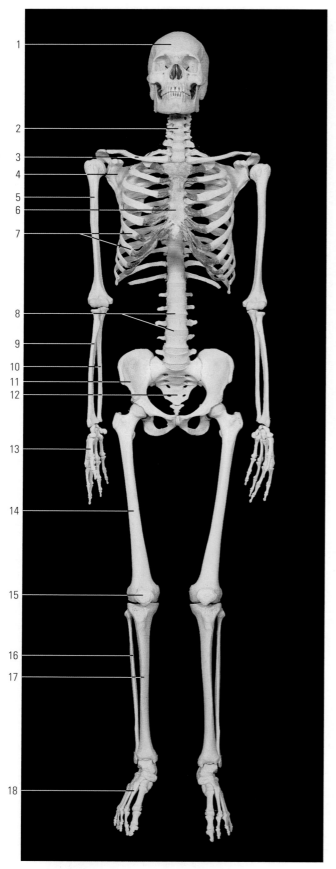

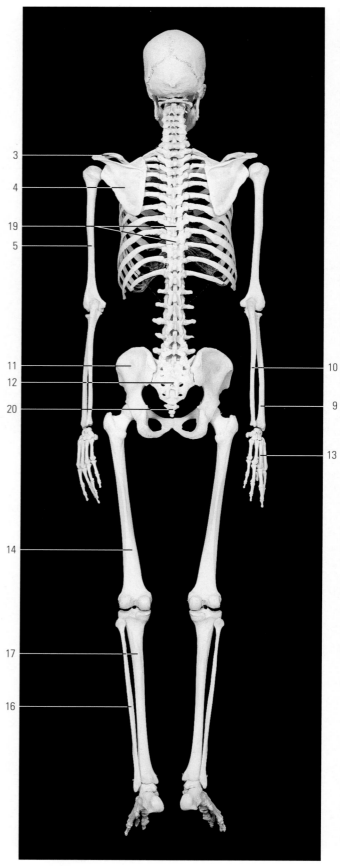

Human skeleton (anterior view). The cartilages of the thorax appear brown.

Human skeleton (posterior view).

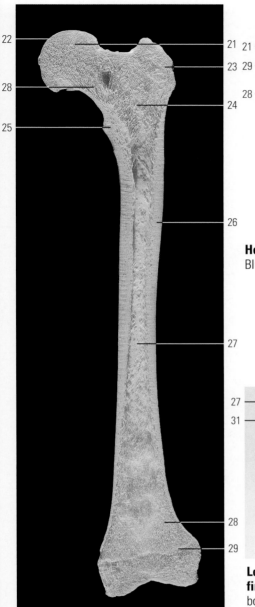

Longitudinal section of a femur. The spongiosa (24) reveals a trajectorial architecture and comprises the bone marrow.

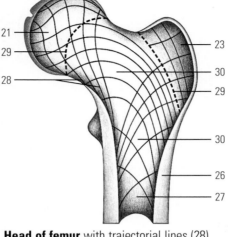

Head of femur with trajectorial lines (28). Blue = articular cartilage.

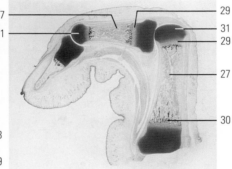

Longitudinal section through a child finger. Red = cartilages. The growth of bones is maintained by epiphyseal plates (29).

1 **Skull** (cranium)
2 Cervical vertebrae
3 Clavicle
4 Shoulder blade (scapula)
5 Humerus
6 Sternum
7 **Ribs (costae)**
8 **Lumbar vertebrae**
9 Radius
10 Ulna
11 **Pelvis**
12 Sacrum
13 Bones of hand
14 Femur
15 Patella
16 Fibula
17 Tibia
18 Bones of foot
19 **Thoracic vertebrae**
20 Coccyx
21 Head of femur
22 Articular surface (in the living covered by articular cartilage)
23 Greater trochanter of femur
24 **Spongy bone trabeculae**
25 Lesser trochanter of femur
26 **Compact bone**
27 Medullary cavity of the diaphysis (contains bone marrow tissue)
28 Trajectorial lines
29 Epiphyseal line or plate
30 Spongy bone and bone marrow
31 Epiphysis (here still consisting of cartilage)
32 Haversian canal containing blood vessels
33 Blood vessels of periosteum and bone
34 Nerves of periosteum and bone
35 **Periosteum**
36 Lamellated bone structure (osteons or haversian systems)

Structure of lamellated bones. The functional unit of the lamellated bone is the osteon or haversian system (36) consisting of differently structured bone layers and blood vessels within its center. The intertrabecular spaces of the spongy bone often contains bone marrow, the origin of blood cells. After fractures, bone regeneration starts in the well innervated and vascularized periosteum (35).

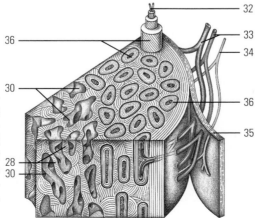

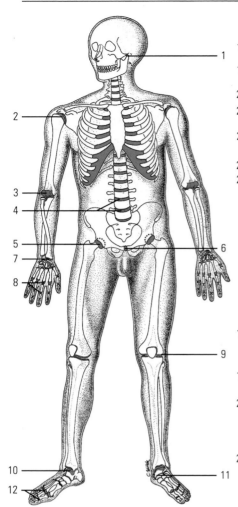

Location of joints in the body. Red = articular cartilages.

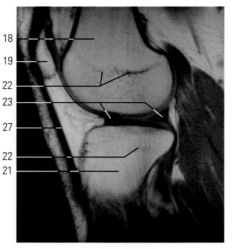

Longitudinal section through the knee joint (MR image).

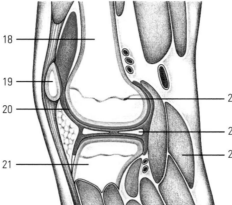

Longitudinal section through the knee joint (schematic drawing, compare with MR image above). Red = articular cartilage; blue = articular cavity filled with lubricating articular fluid (synovia). Note the two menisci (fibrocartilaginous tissue) which are located within the joint.

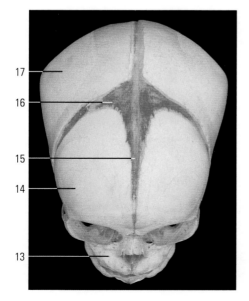

Skull of a newborn (from above). The sutures (15, 16) are responsible for the growth of the skull bones.

1 Temporomandibular joint
2 Shoulder joint
3 Elbow joint
4 Lumbar vertebrae with intervertebral discs
5 Hip joint
6 Pubic symphysis
7 Radiocarpal joint
8 Interphalangeal joints of fingers
9 Knee joint
10 Talocrural joint
11 Talocalcaneonavicular joint
12 Interphalangeal joints of toes
13 Maxilla (part of facial skeleton)
14 Frontal bone
15 Frontal suture
16 Anterior fontanelle
17 Parietal bone
18 Femur
19 Patella
20 Articular cartilage
21 Tibia
22 Epiphyseal line
23 Meniscus
24 Flexor muscles of leg
25 Articular capsule
26 Collateral ligament
27 Patellar ligament
28 Quadriceps femoris muscle
29 Anterior cruciate ligament
30 Tendon of muscle
31 Common tendon of thigh muscles
32 Infrapatellar bursa
33 Bundle of muscle fibers surrounded by connective tissue (perimysium)
34 Isolated muscle fibers
35 Nerve for muscle innervation
36 Blood vessels
37 Nerve endings at muscle fibers (motor end plates)

Structure of skeletal muscle. Each ► muscle bundle comprises several striated muscle fibers (34) containing numerous contractile myofibrils. Each muscle fiber is innervated by a motor end plate (37).

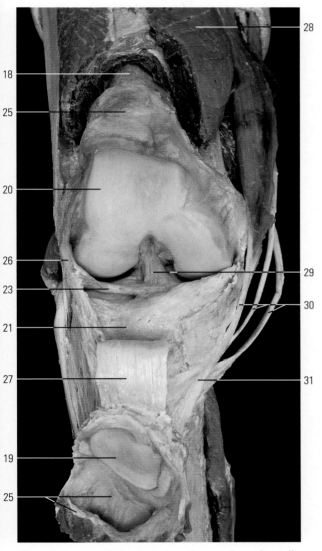

Knee joint, anteriorly opened as the patella and patellar ligament (27) have been reflected. Note the meniscus (23) and anterior cruciate ligament (29).

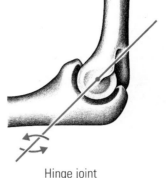

Hinge joint

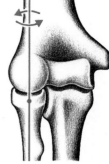

Trochoid joint

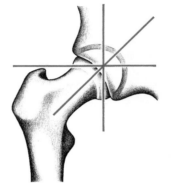

Ball and socket joint

Suture

Symphysis

● **Synarthroses**	– Sutures of the skull, symphysis, intervertebral discs
● **Amphiarthroses** **Diarthroses**	– Carpometacarpal j., tarsometatarsal j.
● **Hinge** (unaxial)	– Humero-ulnar j., interphalangeal j.
● **Pivot** (trochoid) (unaxial)	– Med. atlanto-axial j., prox. radio-ulnar j.
● **Condyloid** (ellipsoidal) (biaxial)	– Radiocarpal j.
● **Ball and socket** (triaxial)	– Shoulder j., hip j.

j. = joint

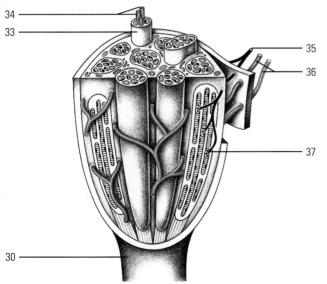

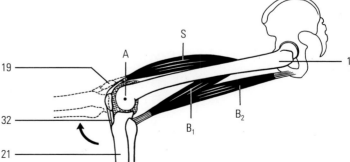

Effect of muscles on joints (here: knee joint).
Extensor (S) and flexor muscles (B) act antagonistically with respect to the transverse axis (A). At the point of insertion, the tendons are often gliding over synovial bursae (32). The patella, a sesamoid bone, developed within the extensor tendon, protects the tendon while sliding over the vortex of the bent knee. Dotted area = articular cavity.

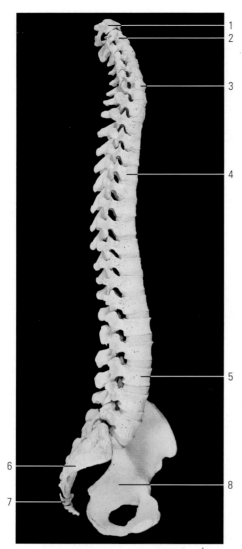

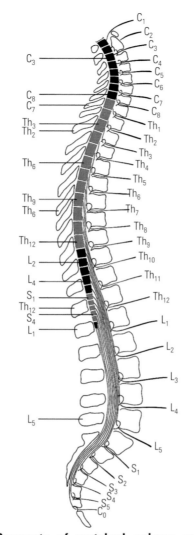

1 Atlas (first cervical vertebra)
2 Axis (second cervical vertebra)
3 Cervical part of vertebral column
(consists of 7 vertebrae)
4 Thoracic part of vertebral column
(consists of 12 vertebrae)
5 Lumbar part of vertebral column
(consists of 5 vertebrae)
6 Sacrum
(formed out of 5 vertebrae)
7 Coccyx (3–5 vertebrae)
8 Coxal or innominate bone
(left half of pelvis)
9 Body of vertebra
10 **Intervertebral disc**
11 Superior articular process
12 Transverse process
13 **Spine**
14 Inferior articular process
15 **Nucleus pulposus**
16 Anterior longitudinal ligament
17 Posterior longitudinal ligament
18 Vertebral canal with nerves
19 Supraspinal ligament
20 Ligamentum flavum
21 **Spinal cord** (medulla spinalis)
22 Periosteum
23 **Dura mater** (green)
24 Arachnoidea
25 **Pia mater** with blood vessels (red)
26 Dorsal root ganglion
(ganglion spinale)
27 **Spinal nerve**
28 Anterior and posterior roots of
spinal nerve (fila radicularia)

Vertebral column with pelvic bone
(lateral view). Note the anteriorly curved
cervical and lumbar vertebrae (lordose) and
the posteriorly thoracic vertebrae (kyphose).

**Segments of vertebral column and
spinal cord** lie not at the same level. The
lumbar portion of the vertebral canal contains only the roots of spinal nerves.

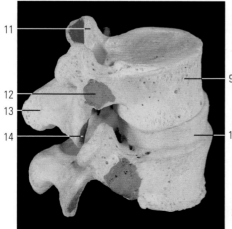

**Two lumbar vertebrae with inter-
vertebral disc** (10) (posterior-lateral view).

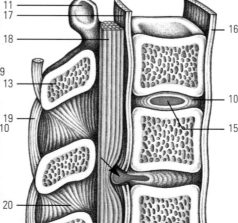

Ligaments of vertebral column. Arrow:
prolaps of nucleus pulposus.

The vertebral bodies are held together by taunt
longitudinal ligaments (thus the S-shaped
flexure of the vertebral column). The nucleus
pulposus can intrude into the vertebral canal
and trap nerve fibers (disk prolapse). The
articular processes of lumbar, thoracic and
cervical vertebrae are positioned differently,
so that the mobility of the vertebral column in
the respective spinal segments varies.

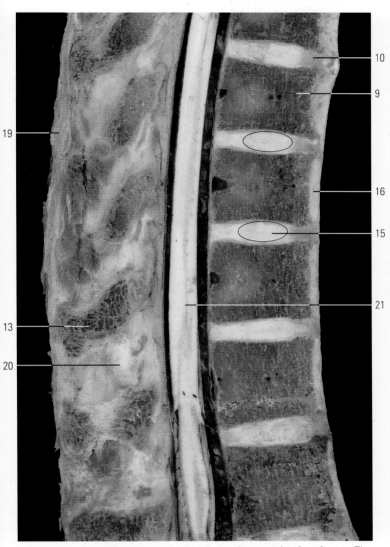

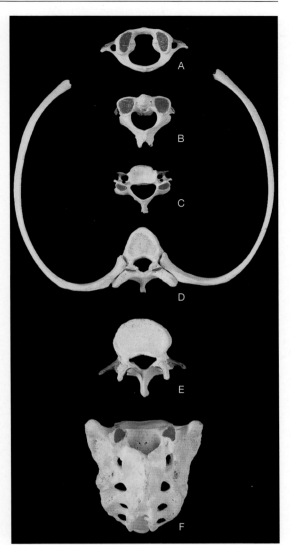

Longitudinal section through the thoracic vertebral column. The body of vertebrae (9) is filled with red bone marrow. The intervertebral discs possess a prominent nucleus pulposus (15) (encircled). The spinal cord (21) is discernible in the vertebral canal.

Different types of vertebrae (from above). Blue = articular surfaces of articular processes. A = atlas; B = axis; C = cervical vertebra; D = thoracic vertebra with 2 ribs; E = lumbar vertebra; F = sacrum.

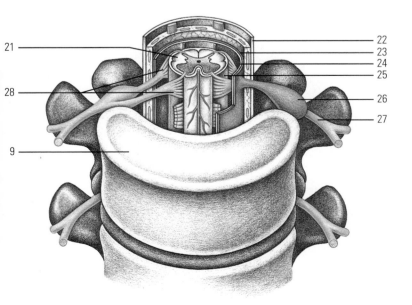

Spinal cord with meningeal sheaths within the vertebral canal (anterior view). The dura mater (green) covers spinal cord and spinal nerves up to the dorsal root ganglion (26). The spinal cord is ensheathed by the pia mater (25) with numerous blood vessels and by the arachnoidea (24). Between the two lies the subarachnoidal space which contains the cerebrospinal fluid.

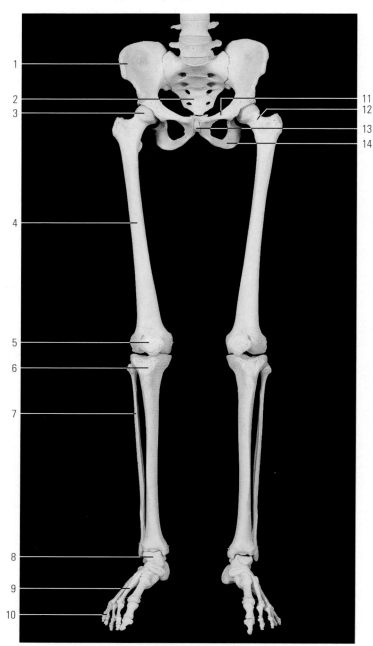

1
2
3
4
5
6
7
8
9
10

11
12
13
14

Skeleton of the pelvis and lower extremity (anterior view).

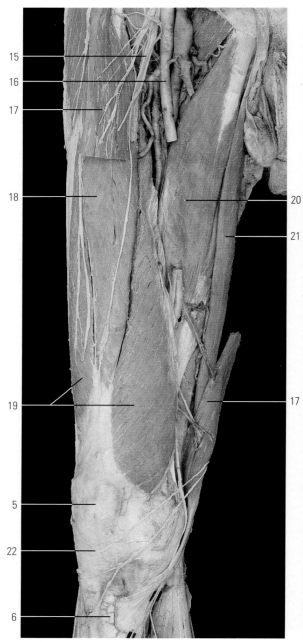

15
16
17
18
19
5
22
6

20
21
17

Muscles of the thigh (anterior view). Sartorius muscle (17) cut and reflected; femoral artery (16) partly removed.

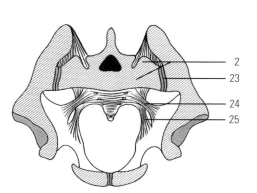

2
23
24
25

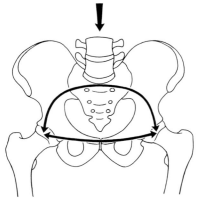

The significance of hip and pelvic joints for erect posture. The pelvic ring divides the body weight between the two hip joints (see right diagram). It is cross-linked with the pubic bone and the symphysis. Symphysiolysis (e.g., during pregnancy) impedes motion. The two sacroiliacal articulations link the sacrum into the pelvic ring where it is tightly fixed by ligaments (see left diagram).

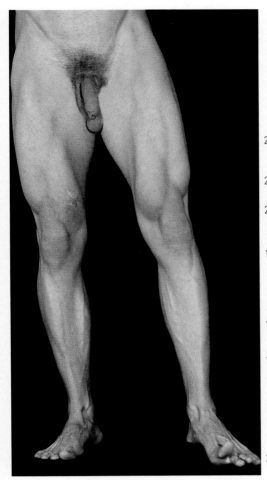

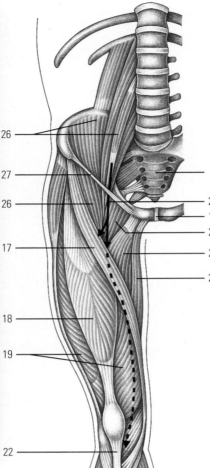

1 Ilium (part of pelvis)
2 Sacrum
3 Head of femur
4 **Femur**
5 Patella
6 **Tibia**
7 **Fibula**
8 Tarsals
9 Metatarsals
10 Toes (phalanges)
11 Pubis
12 Neck of femur
13 **Pubic symphysis**
14 Ischium
15 Femoral nerve
16 Femoral artery (cut)
17 Sartorius muscle
18 Rectus femoris muscle
19 Vastus medialis, intermedius and lateralis muscles
20 **Adductor longus muscle**
21 Gracilis muscle
22 Patellar ligament
23 Sacroiliacal joint
24 Sacrospinal ligament
25 Sacrotuberal ligament
26 Iliopsoas muscle
27 Inguinal ligament
28 Pectineus muscle
29 Course of blood vessels and nerves
18+19 together are termed quadriceps femoris muscle

Surface anatomy of legs. Right = standing leg, muscle intensely contracted; left = movable free leg.

Extensor muscles of thigh (anterior view). Arrow and dotted line = course of femoral vessels towards popliteal groove.

The strongest muscles within the human muscular system are the gluteus maximus muscle, the quadriceps and the gastrocnemius muscle, altogether responsible for returning the leg from a flectional position (against the body weight) to a vertical and thus upright position. The distinct shape of these three muscles make out the characteristic shape of the human leg (bottom, thigh, and calf).

Malformation of the leg. Right = genu valgus (like an X); left = genu varus (like an O). Red dotted lines indicate the respective plans of articulating bones. In the genu varus, the overload in joint pressure is located medially, in the genu valgus, laterally.

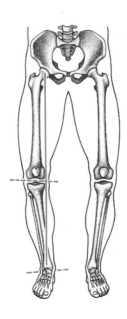

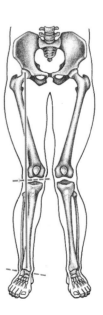

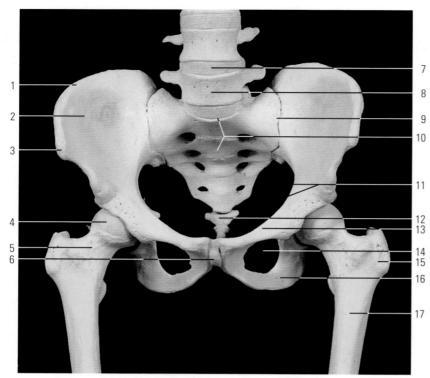

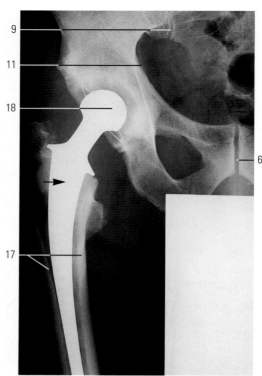

Hip joints (4) **and pelvis** in connection with lumbar vertebral column and sacrum (anterior view).

Artificial hip joint (right side, X-ray image). Arrow = artificial limb, implanted into the femur (17).

The **hip joint** is a three-axial ball-and-socket joint. The movability of the hip joint, however, is partly impeded by a great number of taunt ligaments. Contrary to the shoulder joint, the head of femur lies deep inside the joint cavity (acetabulum), in which results the need for the ligament of the head (22) which supplies the head of the femur. **Differences between female and male pelvis.** The female pelvis is lower, wider, and more spacious than the male pelvis. The pubic angle is wider (more than 90°) and the space between the two ischial bones greater.

1 Iliac crest
2 Ilium
3 Superior anterior iliac spine
4 **Head of femur** (hip joint)
5 **Neck of femur**
6 Pubic symphysis
7 Intervertebral disc
8 Fifth lumbar vertebra
9 Sacroiliac joint
10 Sacral promontorium and sacrum
11 Pelvic inlet
12 Coccyx
13 Pubic bone
14 Obturator foramen
15 Greater trochanter of femur
16 Ischium
17 **Femur**
18 Artificial head of femur
19 Ischial tuberosity
20 **Acetabulum**
21 Iliofemoral ligament
22 Ligament of head of femur
23 Zona orbicularis
24 Pubofemoral ligament
25 Femoral artery, vein, and nerve
26 Obturator nerve

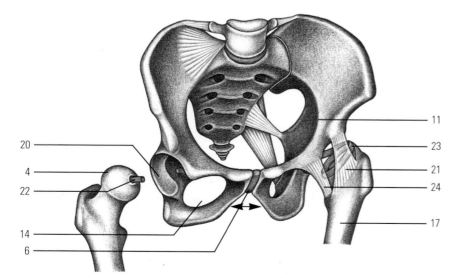

Hip joint and related ligaments. The head of femur is fixed within the acetabulum by a ligament (22). The external ligaments form a screw (23) stretched by extension and relaxed by flexion of the thigh.

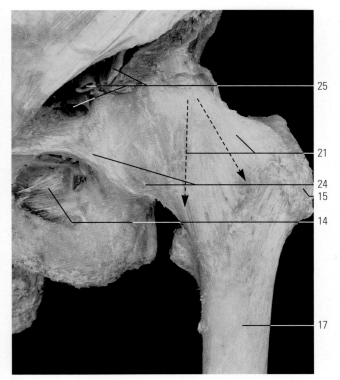

Ligaments of the hip joint (anterior view). The course of the main fiber bundles of the iliofemoral ligament (21) is marked. They become stretched by extension and adduction of the leg.

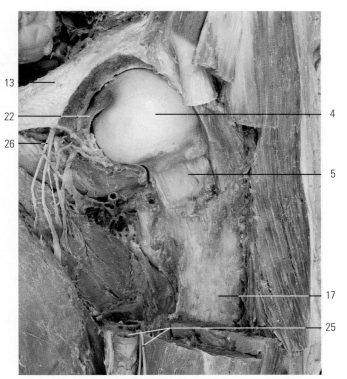

Hip joint (anterior view). The anterior part of the acetabulum was removed to display the head ligament (22).

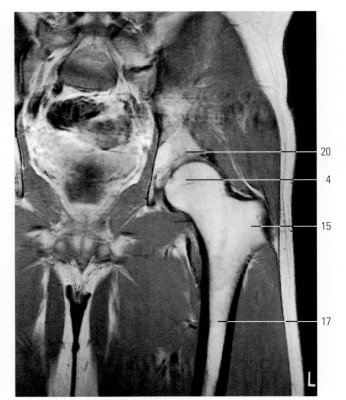

Coronal section through the hip joint (MR image, courtesy of Dr. A. Heuck, Munich).

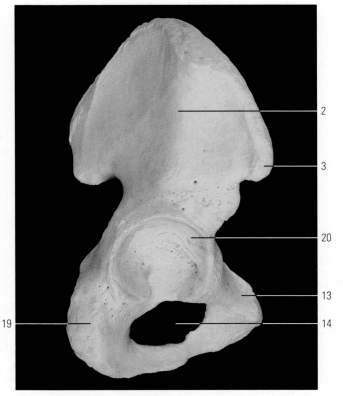

Right innominate or coxal bone (lateral view). Note the change of planes of the ilium (2) (above) against ischium (19) and pubis (13) (below).

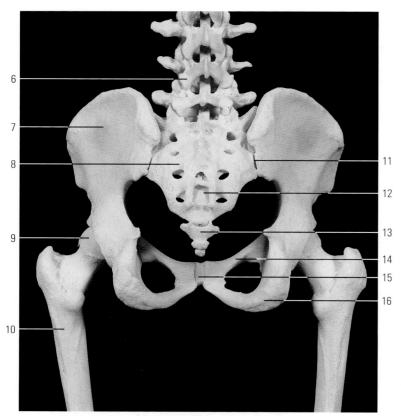

Pelvis with lumbar vertebral column and femur (posterior view). Note the location of hip joints.

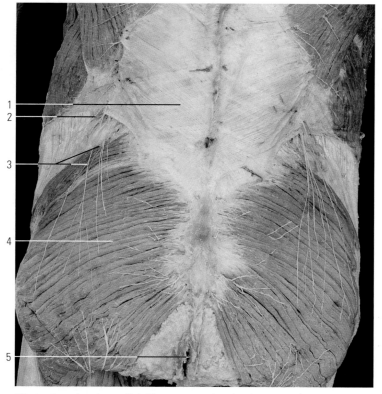

Gluteal region (superficial layer, posterior view).

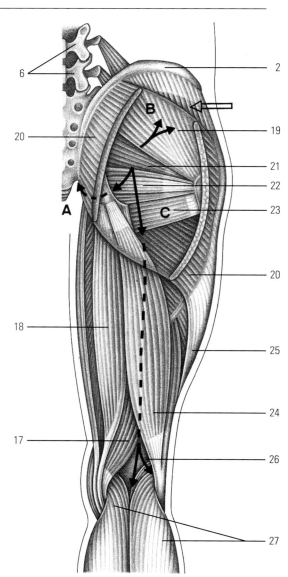

Muscles of gluteal region (deeper layer) and thigh (posterior view). Open arrow = location of intramuscular injection; arrows = **routes of vessels and nerves:** A = route for pudendal nerve and vessels to external genital organs; B = route of superior gluteal nerve and vessels to gluteus medius and minimus muscle; C = route of sciatic nerve that divides within the popliteal groove in the tibial and common peroneal nerve.

The gluteus maximus muscle returns the thigh from a flectional to a vertical position, thus ensuring an upright walk. Consequently, the muscle operates against the body weight, which is why it is so strong.

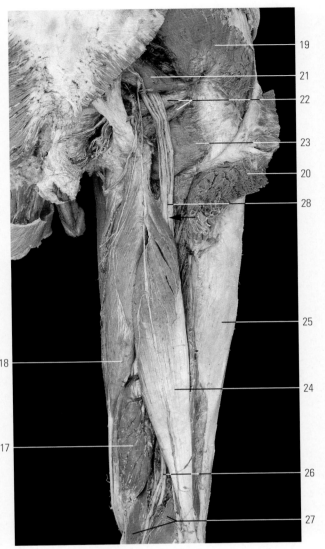

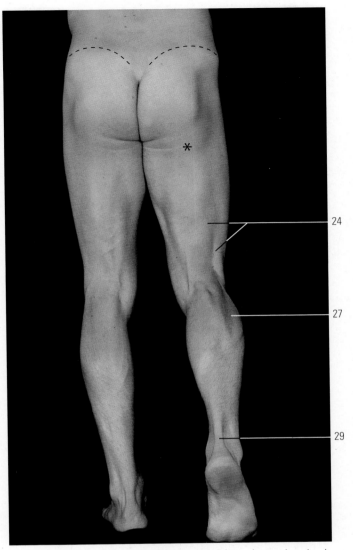

Muscles of the thigh (posterior view).
The gluteus maximus muscle has been cut and reflected to display the sciatic nerve (28). Arrow = site where sciatic nerve can be touched in vivo (see asterisk in adjacent photo).

Surface anatomy of gluteal region and legs (posterior view).
Iliac crests are marked. Biceps (24) and gastrocnemius muscle (27) are contracted, the Achilles tendon (29) is visible. *Touching point of sciatic nerve is indicated by an asterisk.

1 Thoracolumbar fascia
2 Iliac crest
3 Superior clunial branches
4 **Gluteus maximus muscle**
5 Anus
6 Lumbar part of vertebral column
7 Ilium
8 Sacrum
9 Head of femur
10 Femur
11 Sacroiliac joint
12 Sacral hiatus
13 Coccyx
14 Pubic bone
15 Pubic symphysis

16 Ischium
17 Semimembranosus muscle
18 Semitendinosus muscle
19 **Gluteus medius muscle**
20 Gluteus maximus muscle (cut)
21 **Piriformis muscle**
22 Obturator internus muscle (accompanied by gemellus superior and inferior muscles)
23 Quadratus femoris muscle
24 **Biceps femoris muscle**
25 Iliotibial tract
26 Popliteal fossa with tibial nerve
27 Gastrocnemius muscle
28 **Sciatic nerve**
29 Calcaneal or Achilles tendon

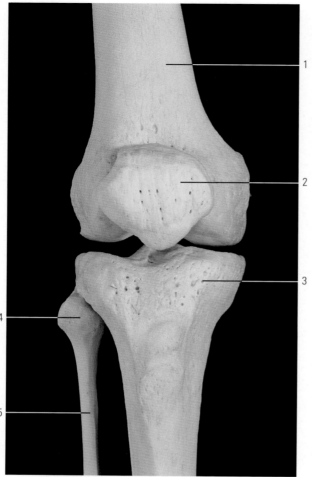
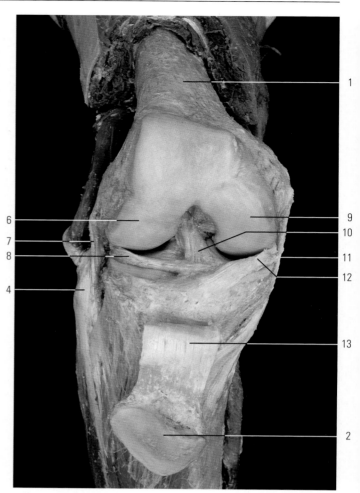

Bones of the right knee joint (anterior view). The fibula forms a separate joint with the tibia. It is not included in the knee joint.

Right knee joint. Articular capsule opened, patella and patellar ligament reflected (anterior view). The two menisci (8, 12) and the anterior cruciate ligament (10) are visible.

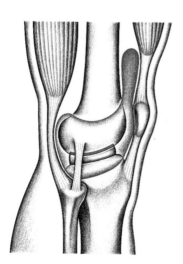
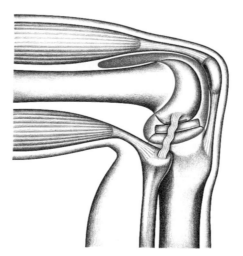

Knee joint, extended position.   **Knee joint, flexed position.**

When the leg is extended, the contact surface of the femur condyles (6, 9) with the **menisci** increases. Thus, the pressure of the body weight is more evenly spread across the tibia (3) to protect the articular cartilage shift towards the back; when the knee joint is flexed, the collateral ligaments relax and the tibia can be rotated somewhat. The **cruciate ligaments** (10, 14) situated within the knee joint secure the stability of the two articulating bones in the flexional positions. Violent torsions within the knee joint, as in football or skiing, may cause meniscus injuries or desmorhexis.

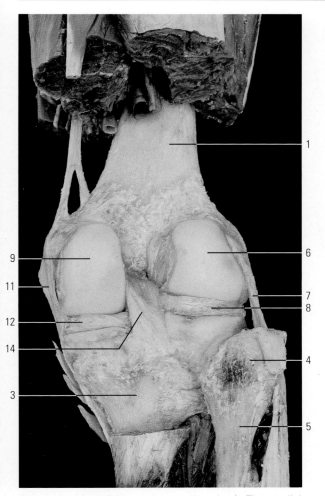

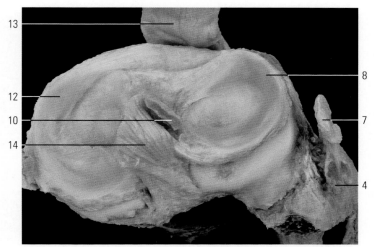

Dissection of the menisci (8, 12) **and cruciate ligament** (10, 14) **of the knee joint** (from above). Note the position of the lateral collateral ligament (7).

1 Femur
2 Patella
3 Tibia
4 Head of fibula
5 Fibula
6 Lateral condyle
7 Lateral collateral ligament
8 **Lateral meniscus**
9 Medial condyle
10 **Anterior cruciate ligament**
11 Medial collateral ligament
12 **Medial meniscus**
13 Patellar ligament
14 **Posterior cruciate ligament**

Right knee joint (opened, posterior view). The medial collateral ligament (11) is connected with the meniscus, but the lateral (7) is not. The posterior cruciate ligament (14) is fixed to tibia (3) and lateral meniscus (8).

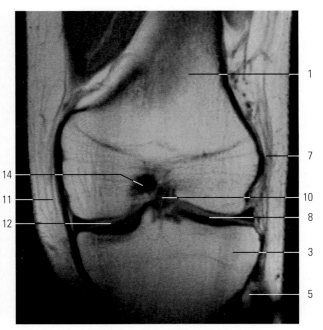

Coronal section through the knee joint (MR image).

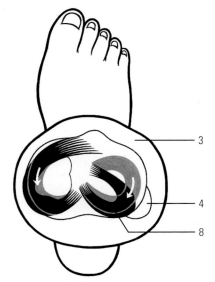

Movements of the menisci, if the knee is bent (arrows). The lateral meniscus is more mobile, the medial is therefore more often traumatized (e.g., skiing or football games).

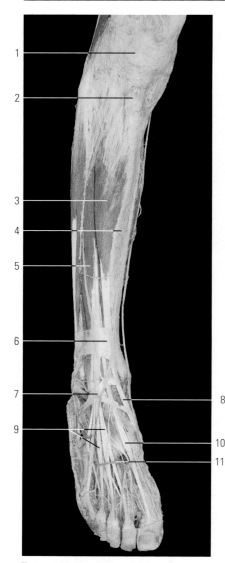

Extensor muscles of leg (anterior view).

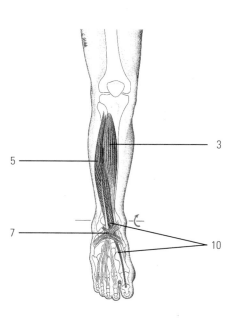

Extensor muscles of leg (anterior view). Red = extensor longus muscle of the great toe.

Deep flexor muscles of leg (posterior view). Note the upper (A) and lower (B) crossing of tendons (tendinous chiasma) supporting the longitudinal arch of the foot. The lower chiasma (B) is located underneath the sustentaculum of talus, keeping the talus in place and preventing the development of a flat foot.

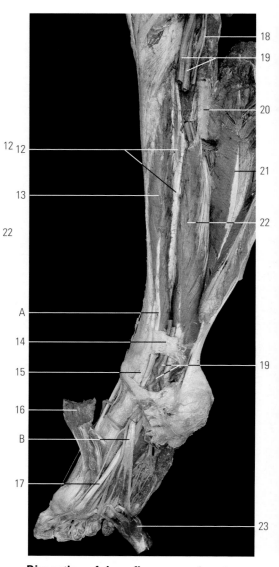

Dissection of deep flexor muscles showing the two chiasmata (A, B) (posterior view, right side). The gastrocnemius muscle has been cut and reflected.

1 Patella
2 Patellar ligament
3 **Tibialis anterior muscle**
4 Tibia
5 Extensor digitorum longus muscle
6 Superior extensor retinaculum
7 Inferior extensor retinaculum
8 Tendon of tibialis anterior muscle
9 Tendons of extensor digitorum longus muscle
10 Extensor hallucis longus muscle
11 Dorsal venous arch of foot
12 Tibialis posterior muscle

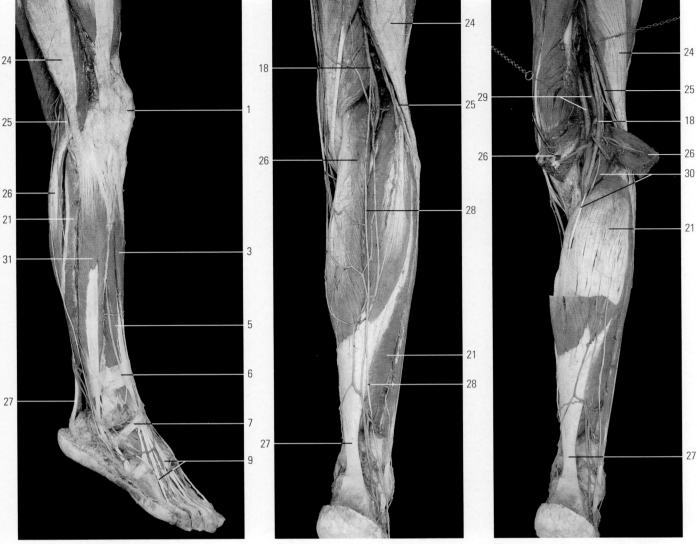

Muscles of the leg (lateral view).
Note the location of peroneus longus and brevis muscles (31). The tendon of peroneus longus muscle passes into the sole of foot.

Flexor muscles of leg (posterior view). Dissection of gastrocnemius muscle (26) (so-called triceps muscle).

Flexor muscles of leg (deeper layer, posterior view). The two heads of the gastrocnemius muscle (26) have been cut to show the soleus muscle (21).

13 Flexor digitorum longus muscle
14 Flexor retinaculum
15 Tendon of tibialis posterior muscle
16 Abductor hallucis muscle (cut)
17 Tendon of flexor hallucis longus muscle
18 **Tibial nerve**
19 Posterior tibial artery and vein
20 Fibula
21 **Soleus muscle**
22 Flexor hallucis longus muscle
23 Flexor digitorum brevis muscle (cut and reflected)
24 Biceps femoris muscle
25 **Common peroneal nerve**
26 **Gastrocnemius muscle**
27 Calcaneal or Achilles tendon
28 **Sural nerve**
29 Popliteal artery and vein
30 Plantaris muscle with tendon
31 Peroneus longus and brevis muscle

Gastrocnemius and soleus muscle both insert on the calcaneus with the Achilles tendon (27). They work together pulling on the calcaneus to push the foot downwards.

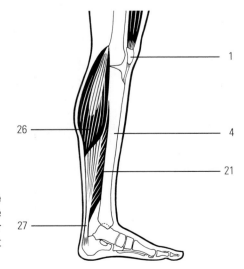

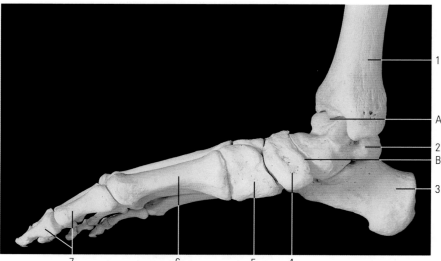

1 Tibia
2 **Talus**
3 **Calcaneus**
4 **Navicular bone**
5 Medial cuneiforme bone
6 First metatarsal bone
7 Phalanges of the great toe
8 Medial (deltoid) ligament
9 **Plantar calcaneonavicular ligament**
10 Long plantar ligament
11 **Flexor digitorum brevis muscle**
12 Plantar aponeurosis
13 Phalanges
14 Cuboid bone
15 Tendons of flexor digitorum brevis muscle
16 Cutaneous nerves of toes
17 Tendon of flexor hallucis longus muscle
18 Abductor hallucis muscle
19 Metatarsophalangeal joints
20 Tendon of peroneus longus muscle
21 Tendon of tibialis anterior muscle
22 Tendon of extensor hallucis longus muscle
23 Flexor digitorum longus muscle
24 **Calcaneal or Achilles tendon**
25 Tendon of tibialis posterior muscle

Bones of the foot forming a longitudinal arch (medial view). A = location of the ankle (talotibial) joint; B = location of the talocalcaneonavicular joint.

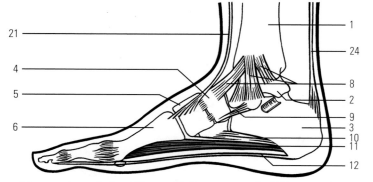

Ligaments and short flexor digitorum muscle (11) supporting the longitudinal arch of the foot (medial view). The medial (deltoid) ligament (8) serves as collateral ligament of the ankle joint.

A = **ankle (talotibial) joint** allows downward (plantar) flexion and dorsal extension; B = **talocalcaneonavicular joint** permits lateral-upward eversion and medial-downward inversion, i.e., rotation or pronation and supination of the foot.

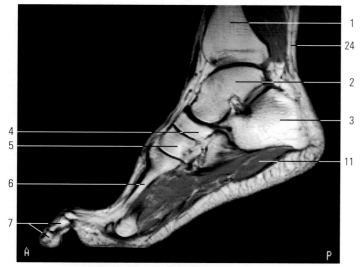

Longitudinal section through the foot at the level of the great toe (MR image).

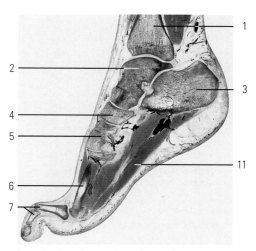

Longitudinal section through the foot (stained plastinated section).

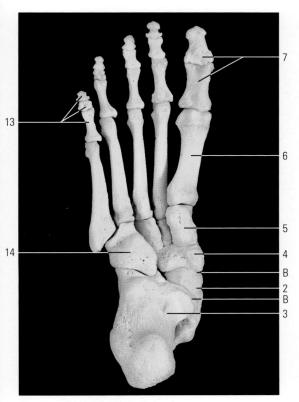

Bones of the foot (from below).

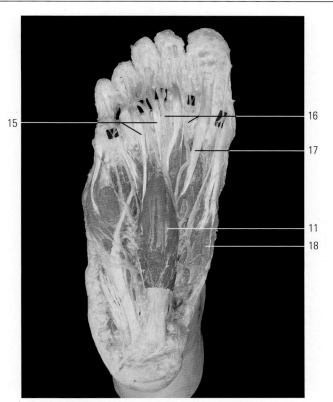

Muscles of the foot (superficial layer, from below). Plantar aponeurosis has been removed.

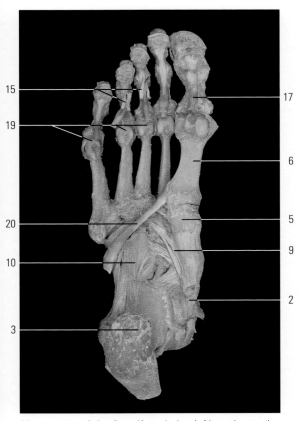

Ligaments of the foot (from below). Note the tendon of the peroneus longus muscle (20) supporting the transverse arch of foot.

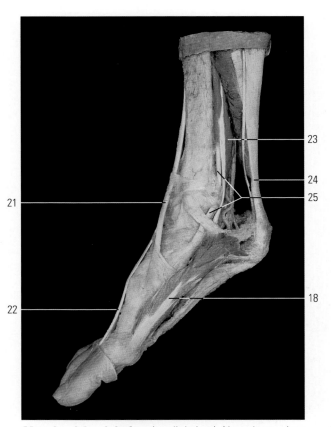

Muscle of the right foot (medial view). Note the tendons of tibialis anterior (21) and posterior muscle (25) supporting the foot arches.

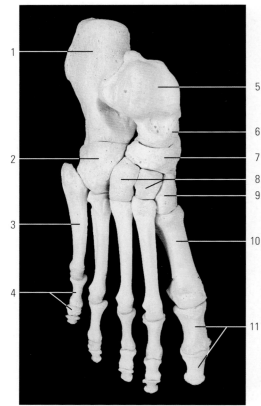

Bones of the foot (from above).

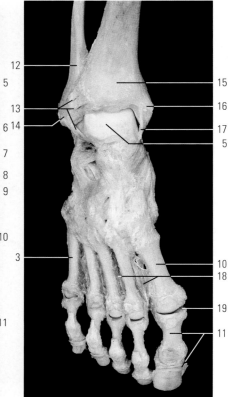

Ligaments of foot and ankle (talotibial) joint (opened) (from above).

1 Calcaneus
2 Cuboid bone
3 Fifth metatarsal bone
4 Phalanges of fifth toe
5 Trochlea of talus
6 Head of talus
7 Navicular bone
8 Lateral and intermedial cuneiforms
9 Medial cuneiform bone
10 First metatarsal bone
11 Phalanges of great toe
12 Fibula
13 Lateral collateral ligament of **talocrural joint**
14 Lateral malleolus
15 **Tibia**
16 Medial malleolus
17 **Medial or deltoid ligament**
18 Interosseus muscles
19 Metatarsophalangeal joint of great toe
20 **Calcaneal or Achilles tendon**
21 **Bifurcate ligament**
22 Tendons of extensor digitorum longus muscle
23 Peroneus longus and brevis muscles
24 Tendon of peroneus longus muscle
25 Extensor digitorum longus muscle
26 Tendon of tibialis anterior muscle
27 Extensor retinaculum
28 Extensor digitorum brevis muscle
29 Dorsal cutaneous nerves (supplying skin of dorsum of foot – branches of superficial peroneal nerve)
30 Great saphenous vein
31 Tendon of extensor hallucis longus
32 **Dorsal venous arch** of foot

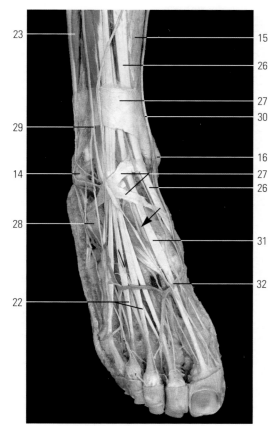

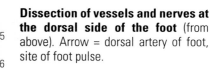

Dissection of vessels and nerves at the dorsal side of the foot (from above). Arrow = dorsal artery of foot, site of foot pulse.

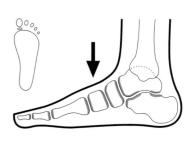

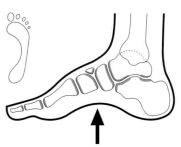

Pathologic changes of the foot.
The longitudinal arch can become flatter (above) or deeper (below).

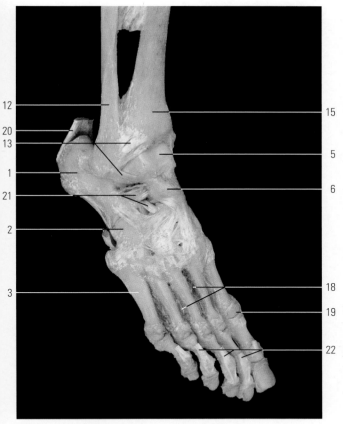

Ligaments of the foot (lateral view). The talocrural joint (5) has been opened and the related ligaments (13) have been dissected.

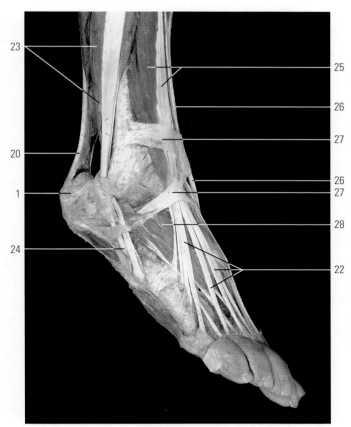

Muscles of the foot (lateral view). The tendons of extensor digitorum muscle (22) are supported by two retinacula (27).

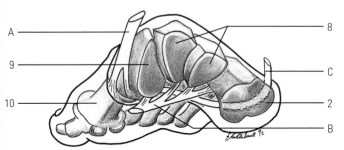

Significance of muscle tendons for the maintenance of the transverse and longitudinal arches of the foot.
A = tibialis anterior, B = tibialis posterior, C = peroneus longus tendon.

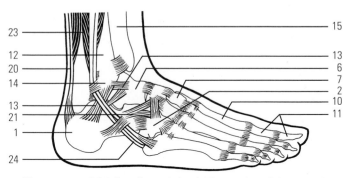

Ligaments of the foot (lateral view). The tendon of the peroneus longus muscle (24) runs into the sole of foot.

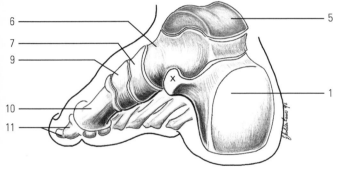

◄ **Construction of the longitudinal arch of the foot.** The talus (6), keystone of the longitudinal arch, is positioned at the calcaneus and its bony process, called sustentaculum tali (×). If the ligaments and tendons, which support the longitudinal arch, weaken, the height in the arch may decrease or "fall". The result is flatfootedness.

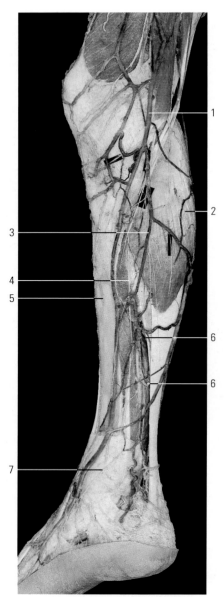

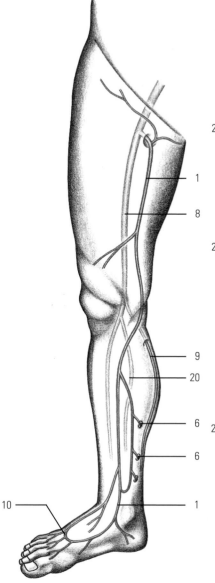

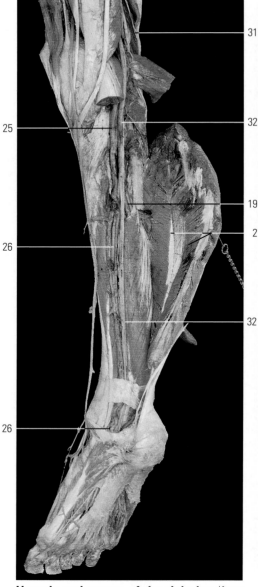

Cutaneous veins of the right leg (medial view).

Veins of the lower extremity (schematic drawing).

Vessels and nerves of the right leg (from behind). Gastrocnemius and soleus muscles have been cut and reflected, to display tibial nerve (32) and posterior tibial artery and vein (26, 25).

1 **Great saphenous vein**
2 Triceps surae muscle
3 Accessory saphenous vein
4 Saphenous nerve
5 Tibia
6 **Perforating veins**
7 Medial malleolus
8 **Femoral vein**
9 Small saphenous vein
10 **Dorsal venous arch of foot**
11 Dorsal cutaneous nerves

12 Deep peroneal nerve
13 Spermatic cord
14 Penis
15 Inguinal ligament
16 Femoral nerve
17 **Femoral artery**
18 Sartorius muscle
19 Peroneal artery and vein
20 Deep tibial vein
21 Internal iliac artery
22 Obturator artery

23 Internal pudendal artery
24 Perforating arteries
25 Popliteal artery
26 Posterior tibial artery
27 Anterior tibial artery
28 Medial and lateral plantar arteries
29 Dorsal artery of foot
30 Posterior tibial artery dividing in the two plantar arteries
31 Common peroneal or fibular nerve
32 **Tibial nerve**

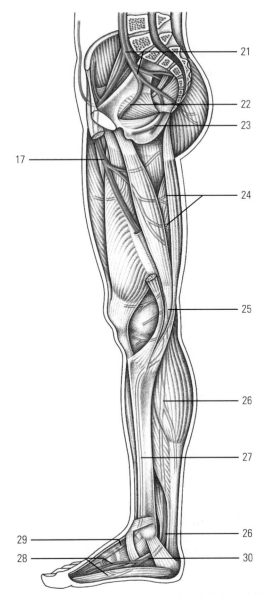

Arteries of pelvis and lower extremity (medial view, right side).

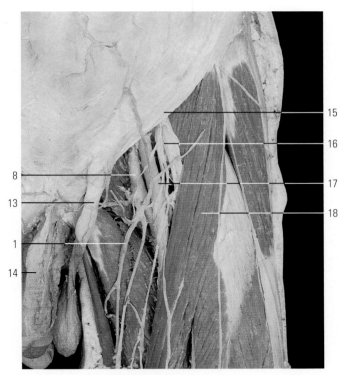

Inguinal region in the male (left side, anterior view). Note the femoral nerve and vessels underneath the inguinal ligament.

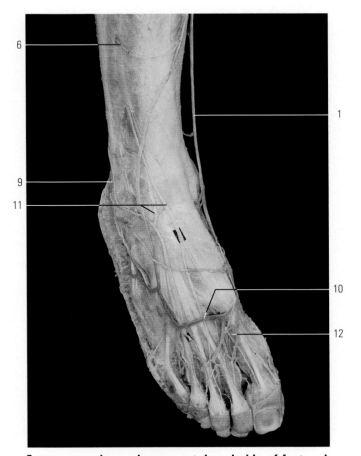

Cutaneous veins and nerves at dorsal side of foot and leg.

The **vessels of the lower limb** travel along the flexor side of the limb, from the inguinal region to the popliteal fossa and from the crural region to the sole of the foot. The vessels run to the sole of the foot behind the internal ankle where they are protected by ligaments. The arteries of the leg are always accompanied by two veins that possess numerous valves to prevent a reverse flow of blood. Perforating veins piercing the crural fascia communicate the superficial with the deep veins. Varicose veins and ulcers often develop at the site where perforating veins pierce the fascia. The venous blood of the foot is predominantly drained by the great saphenous vein (1), which opens into the femoral vein (8) in the inguinal region. Dorsal veins of the foot can well be used for intravenous injections.

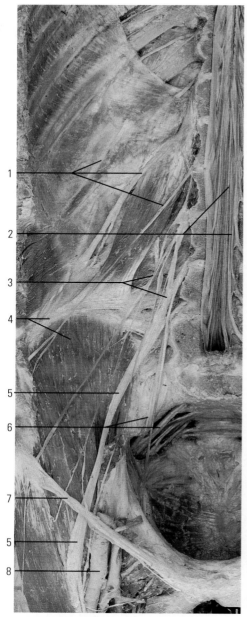

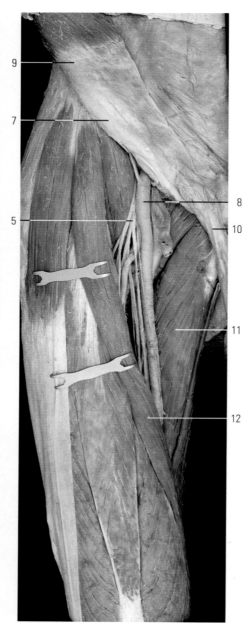

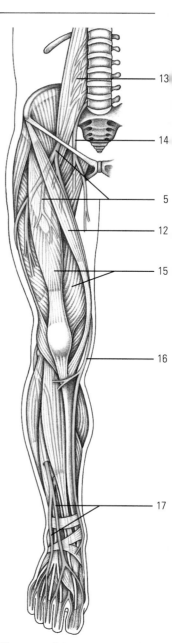

Dissection of the lumbosacral plexus at dorsal body wall (right side, anterior view). The vertebral canal has been opened to display the roots of the spinal nerves (2). The psoas muscle has been removed to show the femoral nerve (5) and the lumbar plexus (3).

Dissection of femoral artery and nerve (right thigh, anterior view). Sartorius muscle (12) was slightly reflected to display femoral vessels and nerve. The superficial location of femoral artery (8) can be used for intraarterial injections or introduction of catheters.

Nerves of lower extremity (anterior view). The lumbar plexus lies within the greater psoas muscle (13). The femoral nerve (5) supplies the extensor muscles of the thigh, whereas the flexor muscles and the entire leg and foot are supplied by branches of the sciatic nerve (lies posteriorly).

1 Iliohypogastric and
   ilioinguinal nerve of lumbar
   plexus
2 Roots of spinal nerves within
   the vertebral canal
3 **Lumbar plexus**
4 Iliac crest and iliacus muscle
5 **Femoral nerve** (innervation of
   extensor muscles of thigh)

6 Sacral plexus
7 Inguinal ligament
8 Femoral artery
9 Superior anterior iliac spine
10 Spermatic cord
11 Adductor longus muscle
12 Sartorius muscle
13 Lumbar plexus within
   psoas major muscle

14 Obturator nerve (innervation
   of adductor muscles)
15 Quadriceps femoris muscle
16 **Saphenous nerve** (innervation
   of skin of leg and foot)
17 Dorsal cutaneous nerves of foot

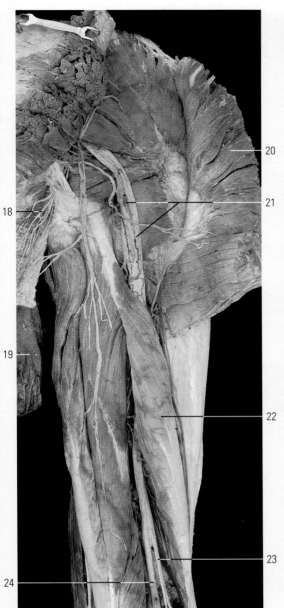

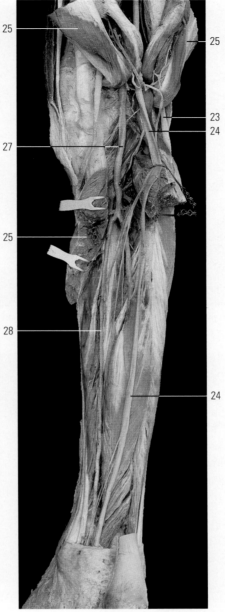

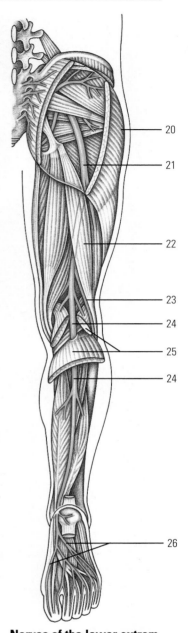

Dissection of the sciatic nerve in the gluteal and posterior thigh region (dorsal view). The gluteus maximus muscle (20) has been cut and reflected to display the sciatic nerve (21). Note the division of sciatic nerve in the tibial (24) and fibular (23) nerve at the thigh.

Nerves of the leg (posterior view). The gastrocnemius and soleus muscles have been partly removed to display the tibial nerve (24).

Nerves of the lower extremity (posterior view). Note the course of the sciatic nerve (21) and its two main branches, the tibial nerve (24) up to the foot sole and the fibular (peroneal) nerve (23) supplying the anterior part of the leg and the dorsum of the foot.

18 Pudendal nerve
 (innervation of external genital organs)
19 Scrotal sac
20 Gluteus maximus muscle
21 **Sciatic nerve**
22 Biceps femoris muscle
23 Common peroneal nerve

24 **Tibial nerve**
25 Triceps surae muscle
26 Medial and lateral plantar nerves
 (branches of tibial nerve)
27 Popliteal artery
28 Posterior tibial artery

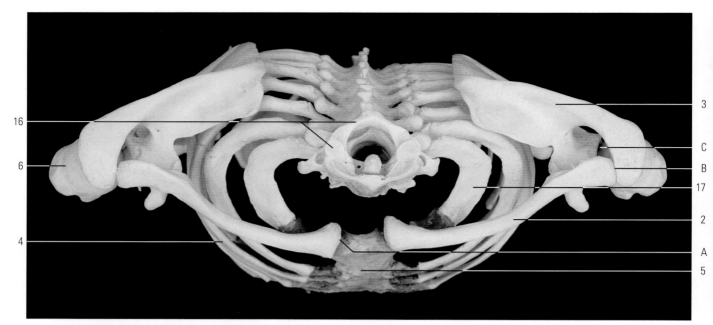

Bones of the shoulder girdle (from above). A = sternoclavicular joint; B = acromioclavicular joint; C = shoulder joint.

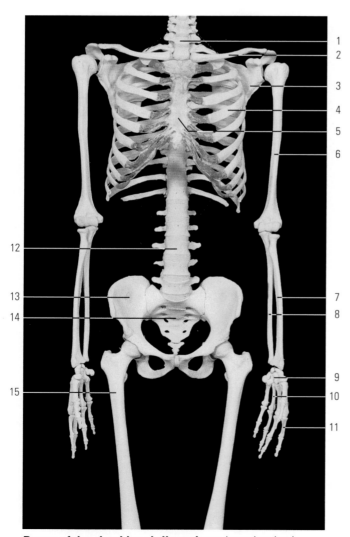

Bones of the shoulder girdle and arm (anterior view).

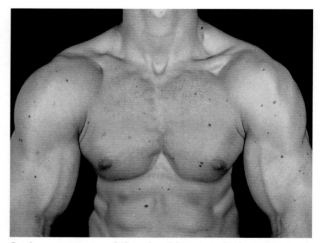

Surface anatomy of the shoulder muscle (anterior view). All muscles intensely contracted.

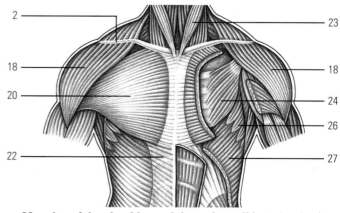

Muscles of the shoulder and thoracic wall (anterior view). Right = superficial layer; left = deeper layer.

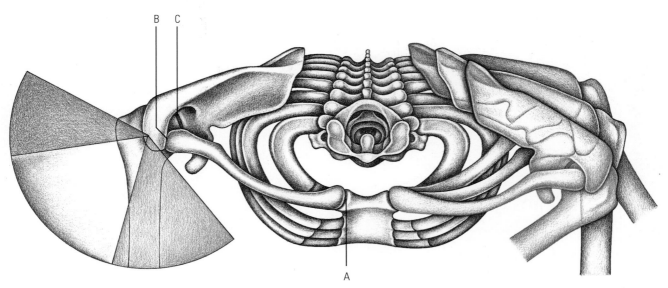

Bones of the shoulder girdle and humerus (from above). Due to the great clavicle mobility in the sternoclavicular (A) and acromioclavicular joints (B), the shoulder blade can be extensively moved upon the thorax (shown on the left side). Movements of the arm in the shoulder joint alone are restricted to the white area (shown on the right side). However, by way of additional movements of the shoulder girdle, the acting radius of the arm can be increased greatly (blue areas).

The three ball-and-socket joints of the shoulder girdle
A = inner clavicular joint (sternoclavicular articulation)
B = outer clavicular joint (acromioclavicular articulation)
C = shoulder joint (humeral articulation)

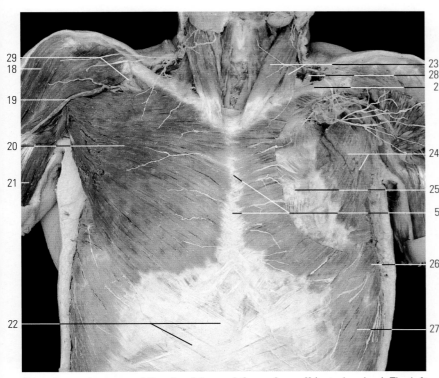

1 Cervical vertebra
2 Clavicle
3 Shoulder blade (scapula)
4 Thorax
5 Sternum
6 Humerus
7 Radius
8 Ulna
9 Carpals
10 Metacarpals
11 Phalanges
12 Lumbar vertebra
13 Pelvis
14 Sacrum
15 Femur
16 Atlas (first cervical vertebra)
17 First rib (costa I)
18 **Deltoid muscle**
19 Cephalic vein
20 **Pectoralis major muscle**
21 Biceps brachii muscle
22 Sheath of rectus abdominis muscle
23 Sternocleidomastoid muscle
24 **Pectoralis minor muscle**
25 Third rib (costa III)
26 Serratus anterior muscle
27 External abdominal oblique muscle
28 Supraclavicular groove
29 Deltoideopectoral groove of Mohrenheim

Muscles and nerves of the shoulder and thoracic wall (anterior view). The left pectoralis major muscle has been cut to display the pectoralis minor muscle. Note the segmental arrangement of the cutaneous nerves.

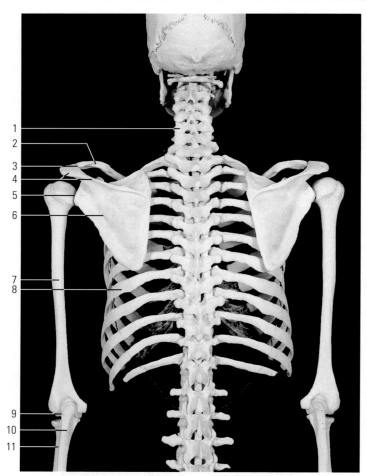

Bones of the shoulder girdle and thorax (dorsal view).

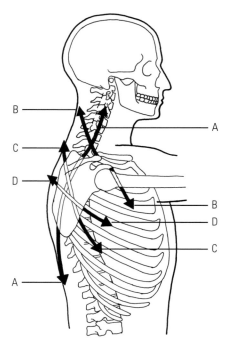

Muscle loops of the shoulder blade. The scapula can be moved by four muscle loops in various directions, thereby considerably enhancing the radius of arm movements in the shoulder joint.
A = levator trapezius loop
B = trapezius pectoralis minor loop
C = rhomboid serratus loop
D = trapezius serratus loop

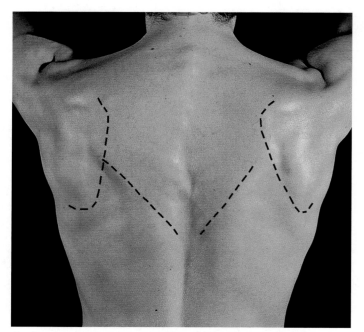

Surface anatomy of the shoulder girdle and back (from behind). Both arms are elevated, the shoulder blade has been anteriorly moved and rotated (medial border of scapula is marked). The trapezius muscle is contracted (inferior margin marked).

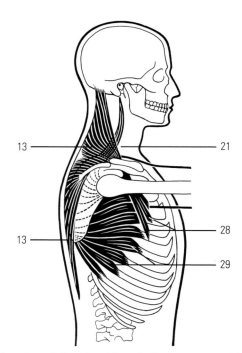

Muscles of the shoulder girdle (lateral view) (see the schematic drawing above).

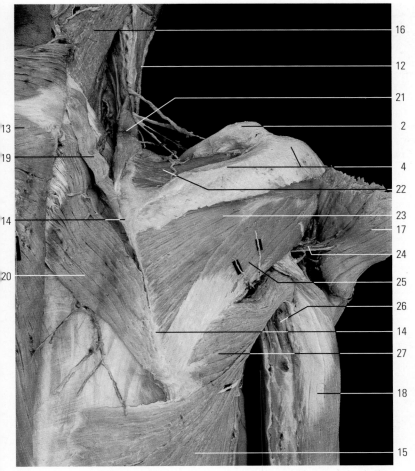

1 Cervical vertebra
2 Clavicle
3 Acromioclavicular joint
4 Scapular spine and acromion
5 **Shoulder joint**
6 Shoulder blade (scapula)
7 Humerus
8 Thorax
9 Elbow joint
10 Ulna
11 Radius
12 Sternocleidomastoid muscle
13 **Trapezius muscle**
14 Medial margin of shoulder blade
15 **Latissimus dorsi muscle**
16 Splenius capitis muscle
17 **Deltoid muscle**
18 Biceps brachii muscle
19 Lesser rhomboid muscle
20 Greater rhomboid muscle
21 **Levator scapulae muscle**
22 Supraspinatus muscle
23 **Infraspinatus muscle**
24 Axillary nerve
25 **Teres minor muscle**
26 Brachial artery and vein
27 **Teres major muscle**
28 Pectoralis minor muscle
29 Serratus anterior muscle

Muscles of shoulder girdle (right side, deeper layer, posterior view). The trapezius muscle (13) has been cut and reflected to the left, to display the muscles responsible for scapula or humerus movements.

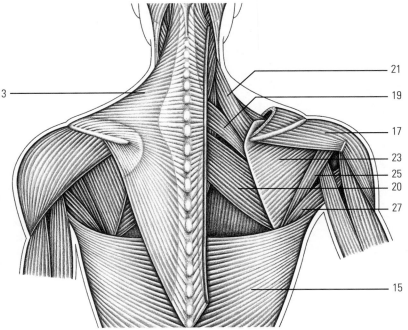

Muscles of shoulder girdle (posterior view); left = superficial layer; right = deeper layer.

The **muscle loops of the shoulder girdle** are needed to bring the shoulder blade (6) into a basic position from which the intended movements in the shoulder joint can be started; e.g., the arm can not be elevated above the horizontal plane unless the shoulder blade has been moved anteriorly with the help of muscle loop D and rotated with the help of loop B (see schematic drawings on page 94).

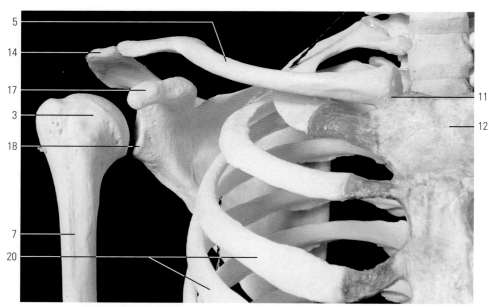

Bones of the shoulder joint (anterior view).

1 Sternocleidomastoid muscle
2 **Acromioclavicular joint**
3 Head of humerus
4 Deltoid muscle
5 Clavicle
6 Axillary artery and vein, and brachial plexus
7 Humerus
8 Hyoid bone
9 Larynx
10 Infrahyoid muscles
11 **Sternoclavicular joint** with articular disc
12 Sternum
13 Lung
14 Scapular spine with acromion
15 **Tendon of biceps brachii muscle** with synovial sheath
16 Shoulder blade (scapula)
17 Coracoid process of scapula
18 Glenoid cavity
19 Long head of triceps brachii muscle
20 Third and fourth rib
21 Glenoid labrum and articular capsule
22 Coracoacromial ligament
23 Epiphyseal line

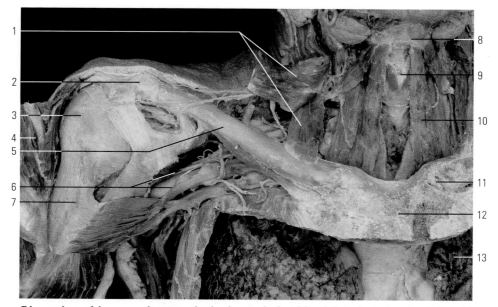

Dissection of inner and outer clavicular and shoulder joints (anterior view). Deltoid muscle (4) has been cut and reflected.

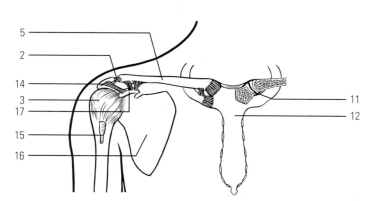

Ligaments of the clavicular and shoulder joints.

The **shoulder girdle** is fixed to the thorax only by the clavicle necessitating a very taunt group of ligaments. The ligaments between coracoid (17) and acromial (14) processes of scapula and the clavicle (5) form a kind of roof covering the shoulder joint which, upon palpation, can be felt as a horizontal ridge. To raise the arm up above a horizontal level, the shoulder blade must be rotated. Acromioclavicular (2) and sternoclavicular (11) joints are three-axial ball-and-socket joints. Numerous ligaments limit their range of motion. In the event of a fall (e.g., from a horse), the protecting ligaments are so tight that a fracture of the clavicle is more likely than luxation of the joints or a rupture of the ligaments.

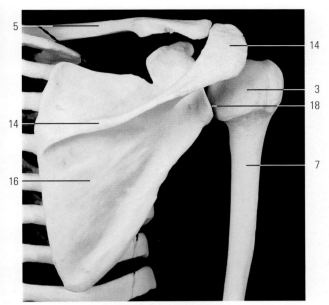

Bones of the shoulder girdle and joint (posterior view).

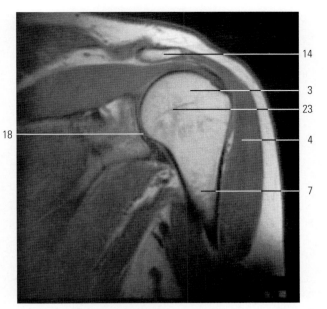

Coronal section of shoulder joints (MR image, with permission of A. Heuck, G. Luttke and J. W. Rohen, MR-Atlas der Extremitäten, Schattauer, Stuttgart, 1994).

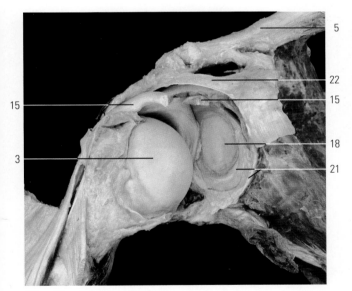

Shoulder joint (opened, anterior view). Humerus has been reflected to display the glenoid fossa (18) and the tendon of the long head of biceps muscle (15) passing the articular cavity.

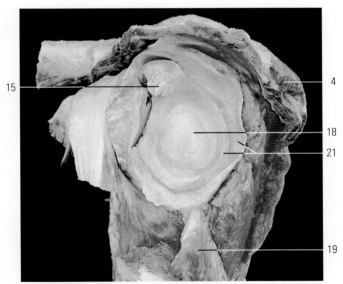

Shoulder joint, glenoid fossa of scapula (anterior view).

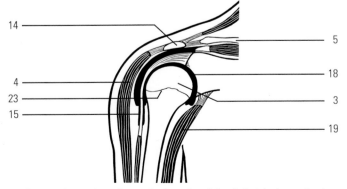

Coronal section through the shoulder joint (schematic drawing).

The **shoulder joint** is a three-axial ball-and-socket joint with a high degree of range of motion. The head of humerus is considerably larger than the glenoid cavity. The muscles surrounding the joint have to be polyphalangeal and strong enough to hold together the two articulating bones. The tendon of the long head of the biceps brachii muscle travels through the joint cavity. Friction is decreased by a tendon sheath which is prone to inflammations.

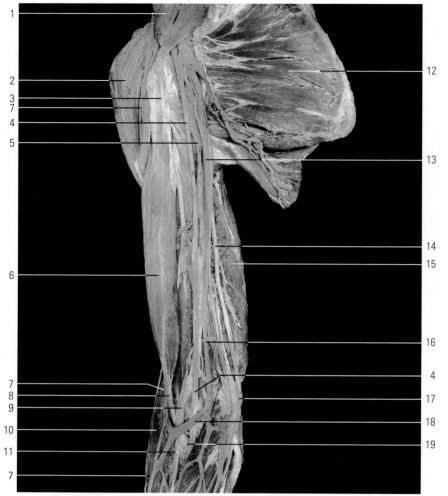

1
2
3
7
4
5
6
7
8
9
10
11
7
12
13
14
15
16
4
17
18
19

Muscles, vessels, and nerves of the right arm (anterior view). Vessels and nerves run at the medial side of the arm within the groove between flexor and extensor muscles.

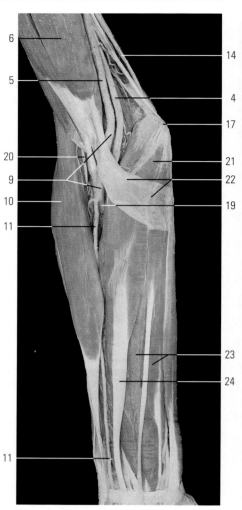

6
5
20
9
10
11
11
14
4
17
21
22
19
23
24

Muscles of the forearm (anterior view). The brachial artery (9) and median nerve (4) run underneath the aponeurosis of the biceps muscle (22).

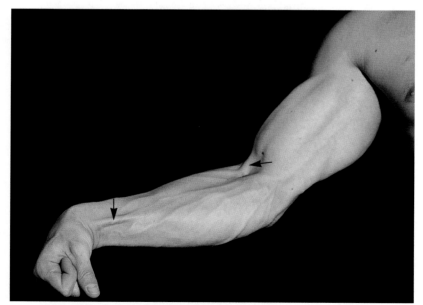

Surface anatomy of the arm. Muscles contracted. Left arrow = tendon of the flexor carpi radialis muscle (24), right arrow = tendon of the biceps brachii muscle (6).

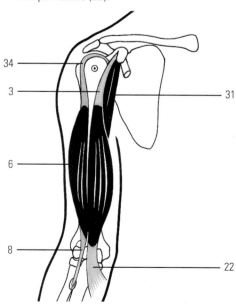

34
3
6
8
31
22

Course of the biceps brachii (6) and **coracobrachialis muscles** (31).

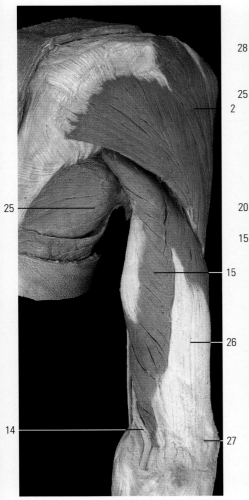

Deltoid and triceps brachii muscles
(posterior view).

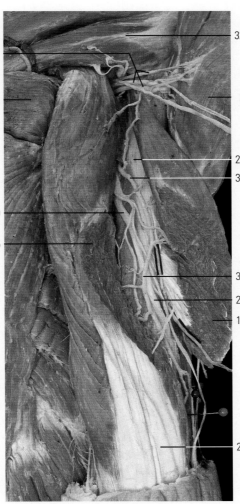

Dissection of the radialis canal (posterior view). The long head of the triceps muscle has been divided to display the radial nerve (20) and profunda brachii artery (30) running within the radialis canal immediately adjacent to the humerus.

1 Pectoralis minor muscle
2 Deltoid muscle
3 Tendon of short head of biceps
  brachii muscle
4 **Median nerve**
5 Brachial artery
6 **Biceps brachii muscle**
7 Cephalic vein
8 Tendon of biceps brachii muscle
9 Brachial artery
10 **Brachioradialis muscle**
11 Radial artery
12 Scapula and subscapularis
   muscle
13 Brachial vein
14 **Ulnar nerve**
15 **Triceps brachii muscle**
16 Basilic vein
17 Medial epicondyle of humerus
18 Median vein of forearm
19 **Ulnar artery**
20 **Radial nerve**
21 Pronator teres muscle
22 Aponeurosis of biceps brachii
   muscle
23 Superficial flexor digitorum
   muscle
24 Tendon of flexor carpi radialis
   muscle
25 Teres major muscle
26 Tendon of triceps brachii muscle
27 Olecranon
28 **Axillary nerve** with
   accompanying vessels
29 Humerus
30 Profunda brachii artery
31 Coracobrachialis muscle
32 Teres minor muscle
33 Radialis canal
34 Tendon of long head of biceps
   brachii muscle passing the
   shoulder joint

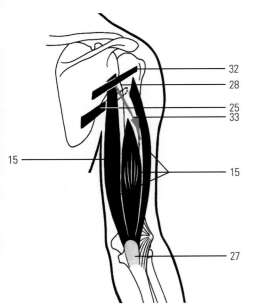

Course of the triceps brachii muscle
and **radialis canal** (red arrow) (posterior
view).

The **radialis canal** (33) at the posterior side of the humerus (red arrow in the schematic drawing) contains the radial nerve, profunda brachii artery and vein. The nerve lies within the immediate neighborhood of the bone so that it can be easily impaired by pressure or bone fracture. The **axillary nerve** runs toward the deltoid muscle via the lateral muscular opening of the axillary region (28).

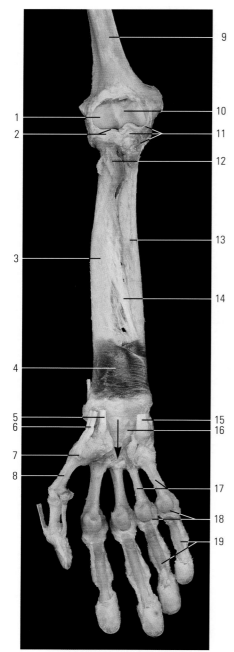

Forearm and hand in supination (anterior view). Dissection of joints and ligaments. Arrow = carpal tunnel.

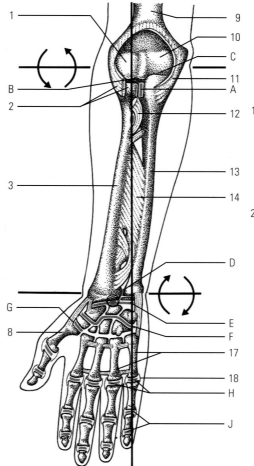

Forearm and hand in supination (anterior view). Axis of joints and related movements are indicated.

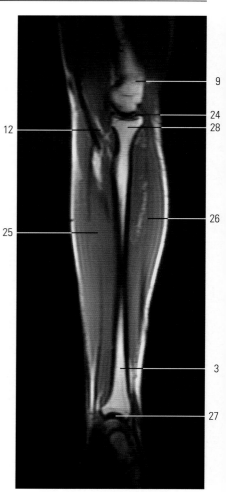

Longitudinal section through the forearm (MR image, courtesy of Dr. A. Heuck, Munich).

Elbow joint (cubital articulation) consists of three parts (compare schematic drawing on pages 100 and 101):
A = proximal radio-ulnar joint – pivot-joint – uniaxial
B = humeroradial joint – biaxial (flexion/extension and rotation)
C = humero-ulnar joint – ginglymus – uniaxial
Articulations between radius and ulna – used for rotation of the forearm (pronation and supination – respected axis is shown in diagram above):
A = proximal radio-ulnar joint
D = distal radio-ulnar joint

1 Capitulum of humerus
2 Head of radius with anular ligament
3 Radius
4 Pronator quadratus muscle
5 Tendon of flexor carpi radialis
6 Tendons of abductor pollicis longus muscle and extensor pollicis brevis muscle

7 Carpometacarpal joint of thumb
8 First metacarpal bone
9 Humerus
10 **Trochlea of humerus**
11 Ulnar collateral ligament
12 Tendon of biceps brachii muscle with synovial bursa
13 Ulna
14 Interosseous membrane of forearm

15 Tendon of flexor carpi ulnaris containing the pisiform bone
16 Carpus
17 Metacarpal bones
18 Metacarpophalangeal joints
19 Phalanges with tendons of flexor digitorum muscles

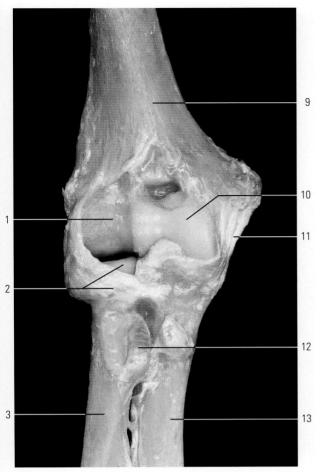

Elbow joint (anteriorly opened). Articular capsule partly removed. Dissection of collateral and anular ligaments.

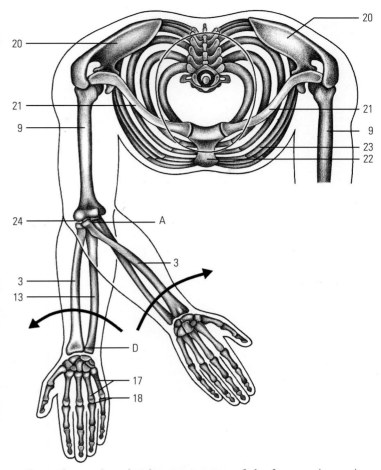

Pronation and supination movements of the forearm (arrows). Note the crossing of radius and ulna during pronation.

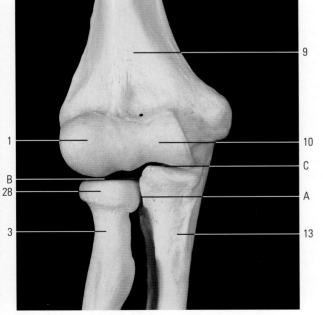

Bones of right elbow joint (anterior view).
A, B, C = location of joints (see table on page 100).

Articulations of the wrist
E = radiocarpal joint (condyloid or ellipsoidal) – biaxial
F = mediocarpal joint – between the two rows of carpals (amphiarthrosis)
Articulations of the fingers
G = carpometacarpal joint of thumb (saddle joint – biaxial)
H = metacarpophalangeal joints (biaxial; flexion/extension and ab-/adduction
J = interphalangeal joints (hinge joints – uniaxial)

20 Shoulder blade (scapula)
21 Clavicle
22 Sternum
23 Thorax
24 **Elbow joint** (articulatio cubiti)
25 Flexor muscles of forearm
26 Extensor muscles of forearm
27 Radiocarpal joint
28 Head of radius

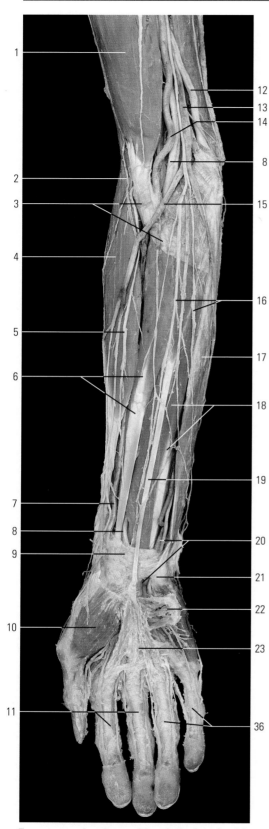

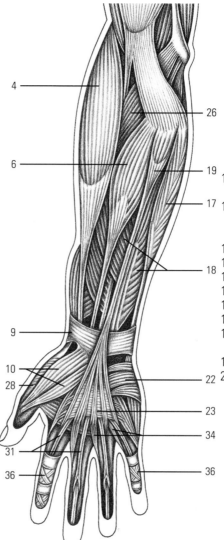

1 Biceps brachii muscle
2 **Cephalic vein**
3 Tendon of the biceps brachii muscle and bicipital aponeurosis
4 Brachioradialis muscle
5 Branch of the musculocutaneus nerve
6 Flexor carpi radialis muscle
7 **Radial artery**
8 **Median nerve**
9 Flexor retinaculum
10 Thenar muscles (abductor and flexor pollicis brevis muscles)
11 Tendons of the flexor digitorum muscles with synovial sheaths and ligaments
12 **Ulnar nerve**
13 Basilic vein
14 **Brachial artery**
15 Median vein of the forearm
16 Cutaneous nerves
17 Flexor carpi ulnaris muscle
18 Superficial flexor digitorum muscle
19 Palmaris longus muscle
20 **Ulnar artery** and **nerve**

Muscles of forearm and hand (superficial layer, anterior view, palmar side of the hand).

Forearm and palmar side of the hand with vessels and nerves (superficial layer). Note the palmar aponeurosis (23) which can be stretched by the long and short palmaris muscles (19, 22).

The vessels and nerves of the arm change their position in the **cubital region** to form new vascular routes in the forearm. The radial nerve extending from the posteriorly located radialis canal joins the radial artery which runs anteriorly; the ulnar nerve avoids the cubital region, running posteriorly to the ulnar epicondyle of the humerus and joins the ulnar artery at the forearm. The vessels and nerves [brachial artery (14) and median nerve (8)] in the cubital region lie relatively sheltered below the aponeurosis of the biceps muscle. A common place for taking the pulse is where the radial artery (7) lies on the anterior surface of the distal end of the radius, lateral to the tendon of the flexor carpi radialis muscle (6). The **median nerve** supplies the thenar muscles and lies medial to this tendon. Here, the median nerve lies close to the surface, which makes it susceptible to injuries (e.g., at suicide attempts and lacerations in accidents). The **ulnar nerve** can be injured particularly where it runs behind the medial epicondyle of the humerus. The palmar aponeurosis (23) of the hand provides resistance during hand grasp and protects the vessels and nerves (especially the palmar arterial arches, lying underneath).

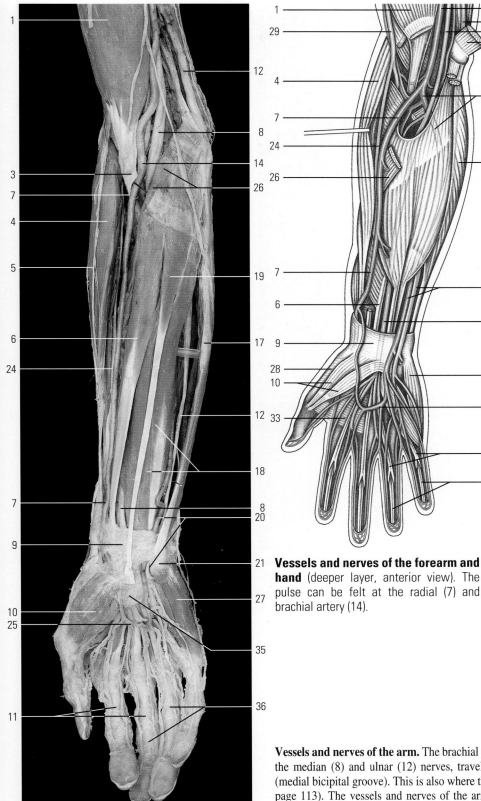

1		14
29		12
		8
4		26
7		30
24		
26		17
7		
6		20
		8
9		
28		27
10		25
12 33		31
		32

21 Pisiform bone
22 Palmaris brevis muscle
23 **Palmar aponeurosis**
24 Superficial branch of the radial nerve joining the radial artery
25 **Superficial palmar arch**
26 Pronator teres muscle
27 Hypothenar muscles (e.g., flexor digiti minimi brevis muscle)
28 Opponens muscle of the thumb
29 **Radial nerve**
30 **Ulnar artery**
31 Tendons of the superficial flexor digitorum muscle (insertion at middle phalanges)
32 Tendons of the deep flexor digitorum muscle (insertion at distal phalanges)
33 Adductor muscle of the thumb
34 Lumbrical muscles (originate at tendons of the deep flexor digitorum muscle)
35 Common synovial sheath of the flexor tendons
36 Digital synovial sheaths of the flexor tendons

Vessels and nerves of the forearm and hand (deeper layer, anterior view). The pulse can be felt at the radial (7) and brachial artery (14).

Muscles of the forearm and hand (anterior view). Brachioradialis (4) and flexor carpi ulnaris (17) muscles have been slightly reflected to show the underlying vessels and nerves (24 and 12).

Vessels and nerves of the arm. The brachial artery (14) with the adjacent veins, as well as the median (8) and ulnar (12) nerves, travel along the inner side of the biceps muscle (medial bicipital groove). This is also where the blood pressure can be measured (compare page 113). The vessels and nerves of the arm (except the ulnar nerve) enter the cubital fossa where they lie protected underneath the aponeurosis of the biceps brachii muscle (be careful with intravenous injections at this site). The muscles of the forearm form three vascular pathways: 1) a lateral path for the radial artery (7) and the superficial ramus of the radial nerve (24); 2) a path for the median nerve between the superficial and deep flexor digitorum muscles; and 3) a medial path below the flexor carpi ulnaris muscle for the ulnar nerve, ulnar artery, and vein, which resurface at the wrist.

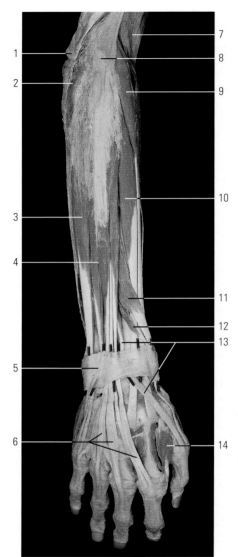

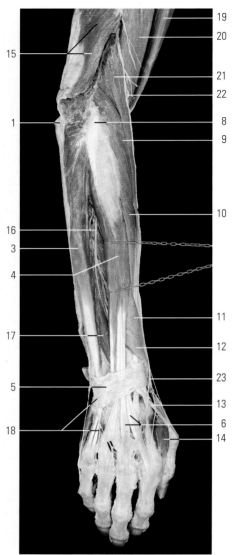

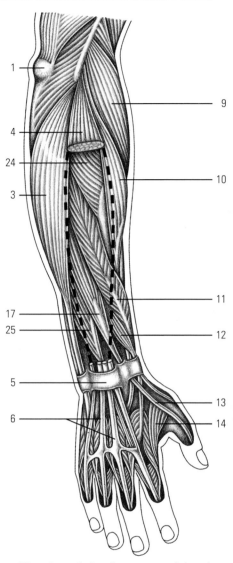

Muscles of the forearm and hand (dorsal side). Locations of the tendinous vaginal sheaths underneath the extensor retinaculum (5) are indicated by probes.

Innervation of the extensor muscles of the forearm. Extensor digitorum muscle (4) slightly reflected to display the deep branch of the radial nerve (16).

Muscles of the forearm and hand (dorsal aspect, deepest layer). Dotted line = location of extensor digitorum muscle (4).

1 Olecranon (elbow)
2 Anconeus muscle
3 Extensor carpi ulnaris muscle
4 **Extensor digitorum muscle**
5 Extensor retinaculum (tunnels for extensor tendons indicated by probes)
6 Tendons of extensor digitorum muscle
7 **Brachioradialis muscle**
8 Lateral epicondyle of humerus
9 Extensor carpi radialis longus muscle
10 Extensor carpi radialis brevis muscle

11 Long abductor muscle of thumb
12 Short extensor muscle of thumb
13 **Tendon of extensor pollicis longus muscle**
14 First dorsal interosseus muscle
15 Triceps brachii muscle
16 Deep branch of **radial nerve** (innervation of extensor muscles of forearm and fingers)
17 Extensor pollicis longus muscle
18 **Dorsal branch of ulnar nerve** (innervation of skin on dorsal side of hand and 2$^1/_2$ fingers)
19 Biceps brachii muscle
20 Brachialis muscle

21 Brachioradialis muscle
22 Cutaneous branch of musculocutaneus nerve
23 **Superficial ramus of radial nerve** (innervation of skin on dorsal side of hand and 2$^1/_2$ fingers)
24 Supinator muscle
25 Extensor indicis muscle
26 Deltoid muscle
27 Groove between triceps and biceps brachii muscle – location of cephalic vein
28 Styloid process of ulna
29 **Cephalic vein**

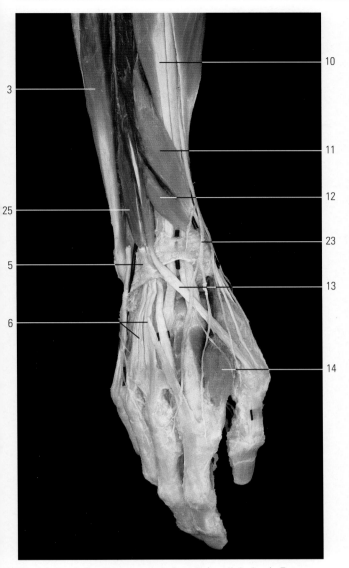

3

25

5

6

10

11

12

23

13

14

Muscles of the fingers and thumb (medial view). Extensor digitorum muscle at forearm has been removed. Note the location of tendinous vaginal sheaths (indicated by probes).

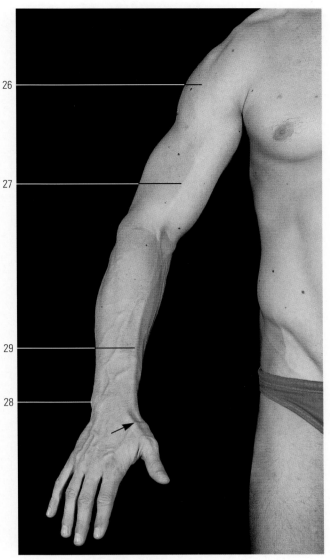

26

27

29

28

Surface anatomy of the arm and hand (dorsal side). Arrow = site of fovea radialis (so-called tabatière) between the tendons of extensor pollicis longus and brevis.

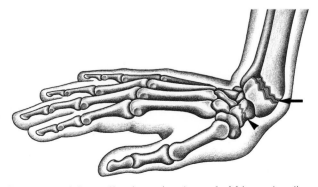

Fractures of the radius (arrow) and **scaphoid** (arrowhead).

The weight-born pressure on the wrist from the arm is transmitted only by the radius. **Radial fractures** (arrow) are common injuries from arresting oneself in a fall (e.g., from a ladder). The scaphoid of the carpal bones (arrowhead) is also prone to fracture.

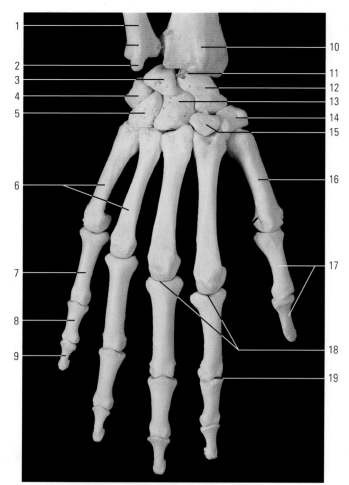

Skeleton of the hand (dorsal aspect).

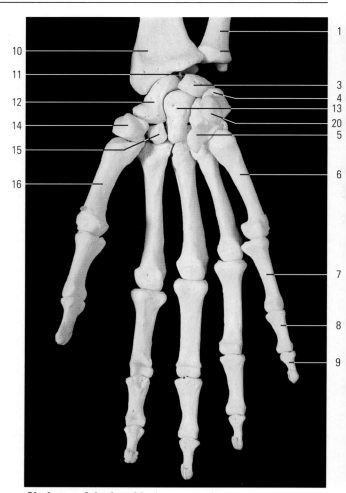

Skeleton of the hand (palmar aspect).

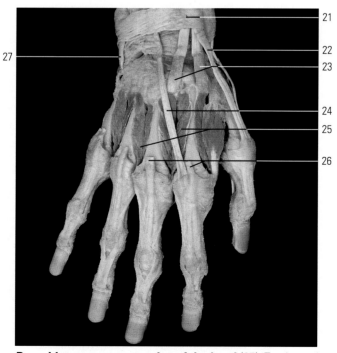

Dorsal interosseous muscles of the hand (25). Tendons of extensor digitorum muscle (26) have been cut.

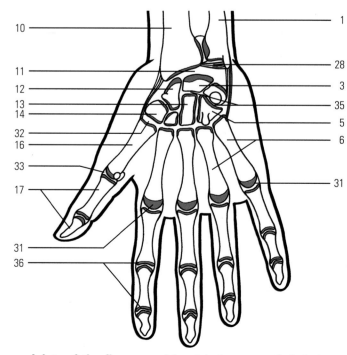

Joints of the fingers and hand (palmar aspect). Articular cartilages are indicated in blue.

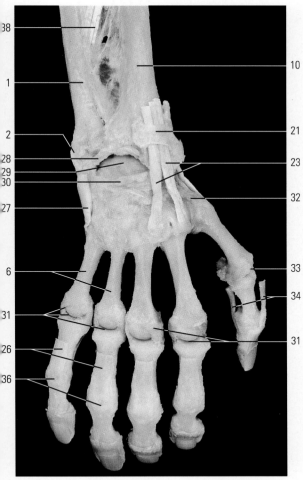

Dissection of radiocarpal and metacarpophalan-geal joints (dorsal view). The articular capsules have been removed and the collateral ligaments (31) retained.

1 **Ulna**
2 Styloid process of ulna
3 Lunate
4 Triquetrum } carpal bones
5 Hamate
6 Metacarpal bones
7 Proximal
8 Middle } phalanx
9 Distal
10 **Radius**
11 **Radiocarpal joint**
12 Scaphoid
13 Capitate } carpal
14 Trapezium } bones
15 Trapezoid
16 First metacarpal bone
17 Proximal and distal phalanx of thumb
18 Metacarpophalangeal joints
19 Interphalangeal joint
20 Pisiform bone
21 Extensor retinaculum
22 Tendon of extensor pollicis longus
23 Tendons of extensor carpi radialis longus and brevis muscles
24 Tendon of extensor indicis muscle
25 Interosseous muscles
26 Tendons of extensor digitorum muscle
27 Tendons of extensor carpi ulnaris muscle
28 Articular disc of radiocarpal joint
29 Carpal bones forming a head for the radiocarpal joint
30 Articular capsule (cut)
31 **Metacarpophalangeal joints** with collateral ligaments
32 **Carpometacarpal joint of thumb**
33 Metacarpophalangeal joint of thumb
34 Tendons of flexor and extensor muscles of thumb
35 **Mediocarpal joint**
36 Interphalangeal joints of fingers
37 Lumbrical muscle
38 Interosseous membrane of forearm
39 Tendon of superficial flexor digitorum muscle
40 Tendon of deep flexor digitorum muscle

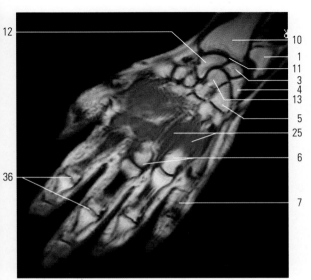

Coronal section through the hand (MR image, permission by A. Heuck, G. Lüttke and J. W. Rohen, Schattauer Verlag, Stuttgart, 1994).

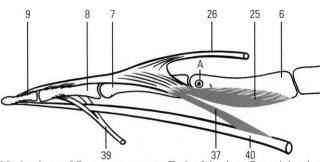

Mechanisms of finger movements. Each of the three finger joints has its own flexor muscle. Dorsally, however, the three joints have only one common extensor muscle acting on them. The extensor digitorum muscle (26), the tendons of the interosseous (25) and lumbrical (37) muscles all enter the dorsal aponeurosis. A = axis of metacarpophalangeal articulation.

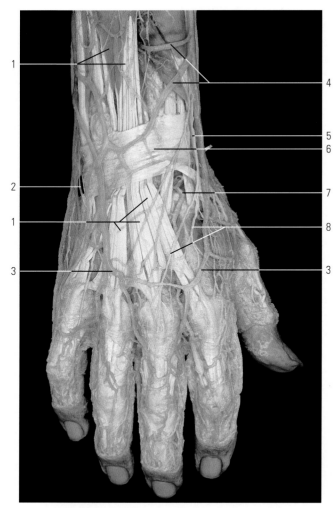

Dorsum of the hand, dissection of venous arch of hand (3) and cutaneous branches of radial (8) and ulnar nerve (2).

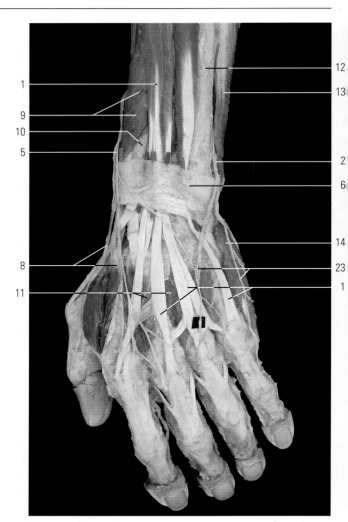

Dorsum of the hand. Dissection of cutaneous nerves and tendinous vaginal sheaths (probes) underneath the extensor retinaculum (6).

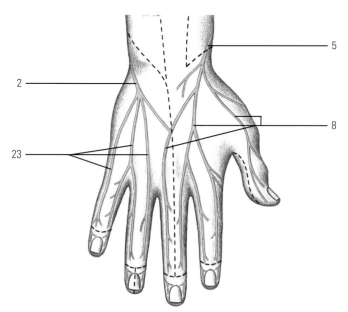

Cutaneous nerves at the dorsal side of the hand. As a rule, cutaneous branches of radial (5) and ulnar (2) nerve supply 2¹/₂ fingers each.

Synovial sheaths in the hand. The extensor retinaculum of the wrist comprises six individual channels for the extensor tendons covered by synovial sheaths. On the palm, however, the tendons of flexor digitorum muscles pass one common synovial sheath mainly situated within the carpal tunnel. Only the tendon of the flexor pollicis longus muscle has its own synovial sheath. Those areas of the synovial sheaths which cross a bone are most susceptible to particularly painful inflammation (e.g., extensor pollicis longus and brevis).

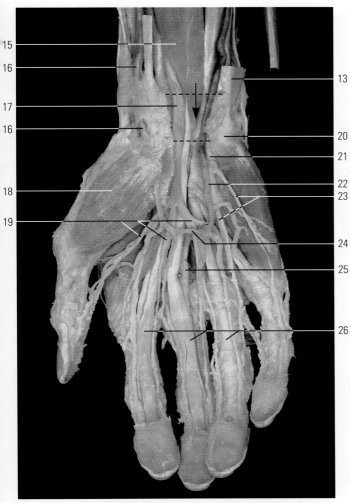

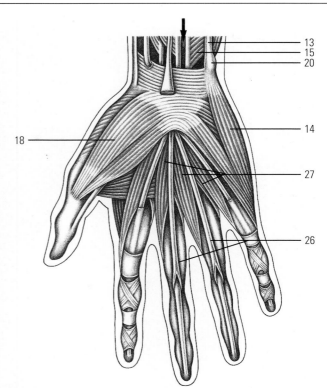

Muscles of the hand, palmar side. At the 3rd and 4th finger, the tendons of the two flexor muscles are shown. Arrow = carpal tunnel.

Hand, arteries, and nerves at the palmar side. The carpal tunnel underneath the flexor retinaculum (dotted lines) has been opened to display the median nerve (17). Note the location of the superficial arterial arch (24) the branches of which supply the fingers.

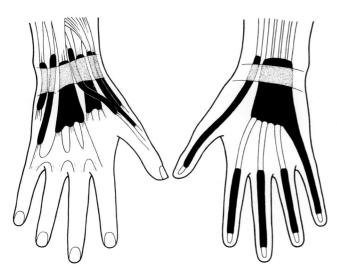

Tendinous vaginal sheaths of the hand; left = at dorsal side; right = at palmar side.

1 Extensor digitorum muscle forming 4 tendons for 2nd – 5th finger
2 Dorsal branch of ulnar nerve
3 Dorsal venous arch of hand
4 **Cephalic vein**
5 **Radial nerve**
6 Extensor retinaculum forming synovial tunnels for tendons of extensor muscles (probes)
7 Branch of radial artery
8 Cutaneous branches of radial nerve (innervation of $2^{1}/_{2}$ fingers)
9 Abductor pollicis longus and extensor pollicis brevis muscles
10 **Radius**
11 Interosseus muscles
12 **Ulna**
13 Extensor carpi ulnaris muscle
14 Abductor digiti minimi muscle
15 Superficial flexor digitorum muscle
16 **Radial artery**
17 **Median nerve** entering the carpal tunnel (arrow)
18 Abductor pollicis brevis muscle
19 Cutaneous branches of median nerve (innervation of $3^{1}/_{2}$ fingers)
20 Pisiform bone
21 **Ulnar artery**
23 Cutaneous branches of ulnar nerve (innervation of $1^{1}/_{2}$ fingers)
24 Superficial palmar arch (arterial supply of hand and fingers)
25 Tendons of deep flexor digitorum muscle
26 Dividing tendons of superficial flexor digitorum muscle
27 Lumbricales muscles

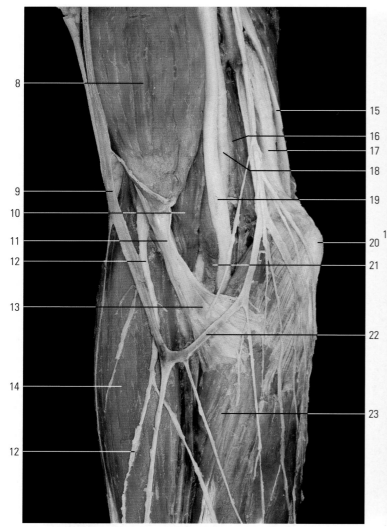

Elbow region, superficial veins and nerves (anterior view). Note the location of median cubital vein (22), often used for intravenous injections.

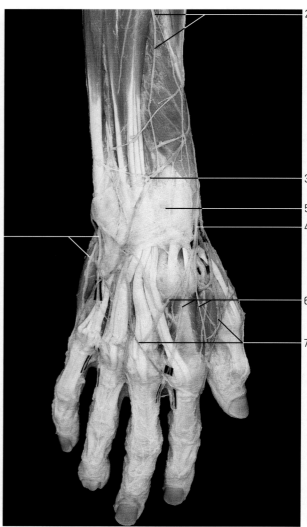

Dorsal side of the hand and forearm. The superficial veins (7) are filled with blue resin.

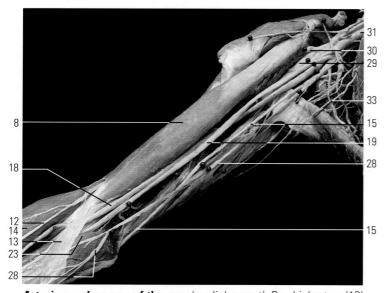

Arteries and nerves of the arm (medial aspect). Brachial artery (18) and median nerve (19) run together in the medial bicipital groove.

1 Cutaneous branches of ulnar nerve (for 3rd – 5th fingers)
2 Cutaneous branch of musculocutaneus nerve
3 Beginning of cephalic vein
4 Superficial branch of radial nerve
5 Extensor retinaculum
6 Cutaneous branches of radial nerve (for 1st – 3rd fingers)
7 Dorsal venous network of hand
8 Biceps brachii muscle
9 **Cephalic vein** (entering the bicipital groove)
10 Brachialis muscle
11 Tendon of biceps brachii muscle
12 Branch of lateral cutaneous nerve of forearm
13 Bicipital aponeurosis
14 Brachioradialis muscle
15 **Ulnar nerve**
16 **Basilica vein**
17 Medial intermuscular septum of arm
18 **Brachial artery**
19 **Median nerve**
20 Medial epicondyle of humerus

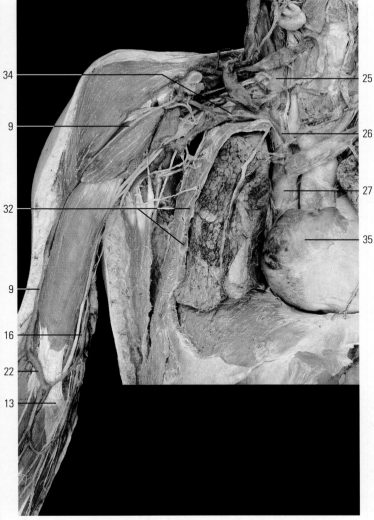

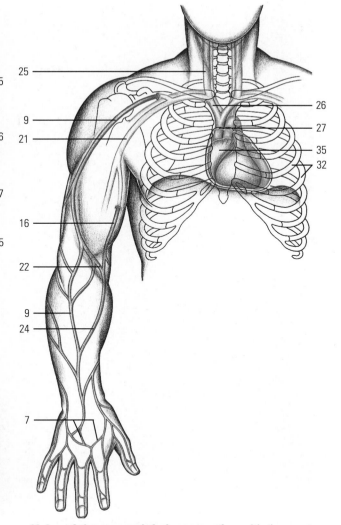

Arm veins and their connection with the heart. The cephalic vein (9) enters the subclavian vein (34) underneath the clavicle. This route can be used for insertion of catheters or pacemaker devices.

Veins of the arm and their connection with the great vessels of the heart. Intravenous injections can be made at the dorsal venous arch of hand (7), at cubital veins (22) and underneath the clavicle into the subclavian vein.

21 **Brachial vein**
22 **Median cubital vein**
23 Pronator teres muscle
24 Median vein of forearm
25 Internal jugular vein
26 Right brachiocephalic vein
27 Superior vena cava
28 Medial cutaneous nerve of forearm
29 Radial nerve
30 Axillary nerve
31 Subclavian artery
32 Thorax
33 Latissimus dorsi and teres major muscles
34 Subclavian vein
35 Right atrium of heart

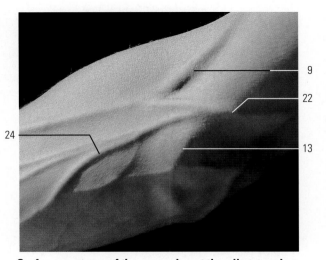

Surface anatomy of the arm veins at the elbow region (anterior view).

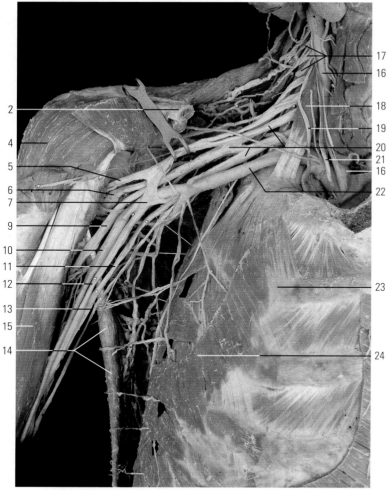

Dissection of the brachial plexus in relation to the subclavian artery (22) (right axillary region, anterior view). The lateral trunk of the plexus has been elevated to display the posterior fascicle that splits into the radial (9) and axillary (6) nerves. Clavicle has been cut.

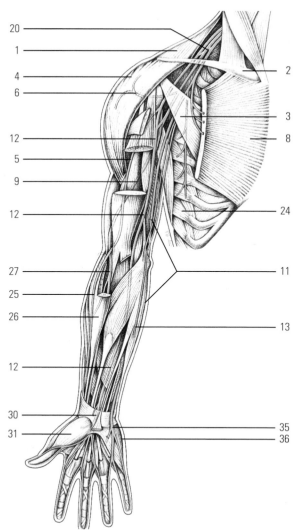

Nerves of the arm (anterior view). Biceps and brachioradialis muscle fenestrated, pectoralis major muscle (8) cut.

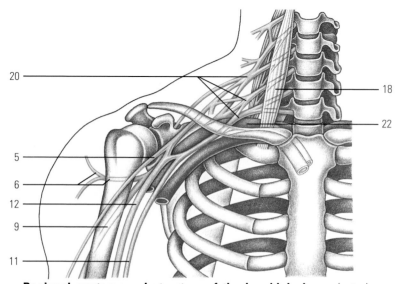

Regional anatomy and structure of the brachial plexus (anterior view).

1 Trapezius muscle
2 Clavicle
3 Pectoralis minor muscle
4 Deltoid muscle
5 **Musculocutaneus nerve**
6 **Axillary nerve**
7 Medial and lateral roots forming median nerve
8 Pectoralis major muscle
9 **Radial nerve**
10 **Brachial artery**
11 **Ulnar nerve**
12 **Median nerve**
13 Medial cutaneous nerve of forearm
14 Latissimus dorsi muscle
15 Biceps brachii muscle
16 Common carotid artery
17 **Cervical plexus** (C_1-C_4)
18 Scalenus anterior muscle
19 Phrenic nerve
20 **Brachial plexus** (C_5-Th_1)

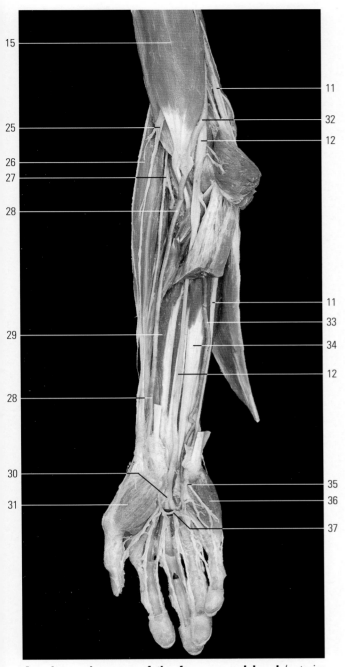

Arteries and nerves of the forearm and hand (anterior view). Superficial flexor muscles have been cut or reflected to display vessels and nerves at the deeper layer.

Paralysis of the radial nerve

Paralysis of the ulnar nerve

Paralysis of the median nerve

Characteristic positions of the hand after paralysis of arm nerves.

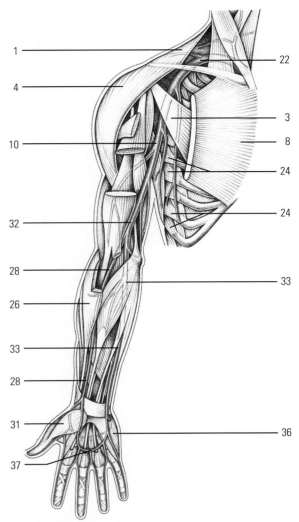

Arteries of the arm (anterior view) (schematic drawing).

21 Vagus nerve (n. X)
22 **Subclavian artery**
23 Second rib
24 Serratus anterior muscle
25 Lateral cutaneous nerve of forearm
26 Brachioradialis muscle
27 **Radial nerve** (dividing in superficial and deep branch)
28 **Radial artery**
29 Flexor pollicis longus muscle
30 Median nerve (situated within the carpal tunnel – sensory innervation of 3$\frac{1}{2}$ fingers)
31 Thenar muscles of hand
32 Brachial artery
33 **Ulnar artery**
34 Flexor digitorum profundus muscle
35 Ulnar nerve (sensory innervation of 1$\frac{1}{2}$ fingers)
36 Hypothenar muscles of hand
37 Superficial palmar arch

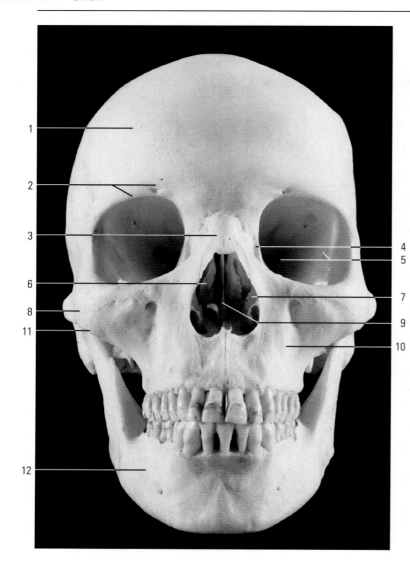

Human skull of the adult (anterior view).

Compositions of the skull

Calvaria – cranial bones
- Squama of frontal bone
- Parietal bone
- Occipital bone
- Squama of temporal bone

Base of skull
- Orbital part of frontal bone
- Sphenoid
- Petrous part of temporal bone
- Basilar part of occipital bone

Facial bones
- Nasal bone
- Lacrimal bone
- Ethmoid bone
- Inferior nasal concha
- Vomer
- Maxilla
- Palatine
- Mandible
- Zygomatic bone

1 Frontal bone
2 Superciliary arch
3 Nasal bone
4 Lacrimal bone
5 **Orbita** (note: superior orbital fissure –
   the connection with cranial cavity)
6 Ethmoid bone
7 Inferior nasal concha
8 Zygomatic bone
9 Vomer (part of bony nasal septum)
10 **Maxilla**
11 Condylar process of mandible
12 **Mandible**
13 Parietal bone
14 Occipital bone
15 Temporal bone
16 Tympanic part of temporal bone
17 Mastoid process of temporal bone
18 Ala major of sphenoid bone
19 Pterygoid process of sphenoid bone
20 Palatine bone

Sutures of skull
21 Coronal suture
22 Sagittal suture
23 Lambdoid suture

Fontanelles
24 Anterior fontanelle
25 Posterior fontanelle
26 Sphenoid fontanelle
27 Mastoid fontanelle

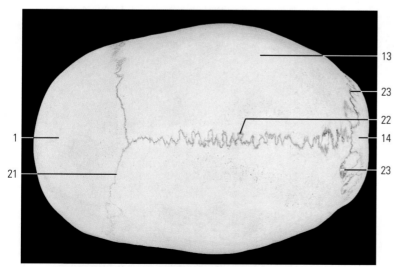

Calvaria of the adult human skull (from above). Frontal bone to the left.
Note the system of skull sutures.

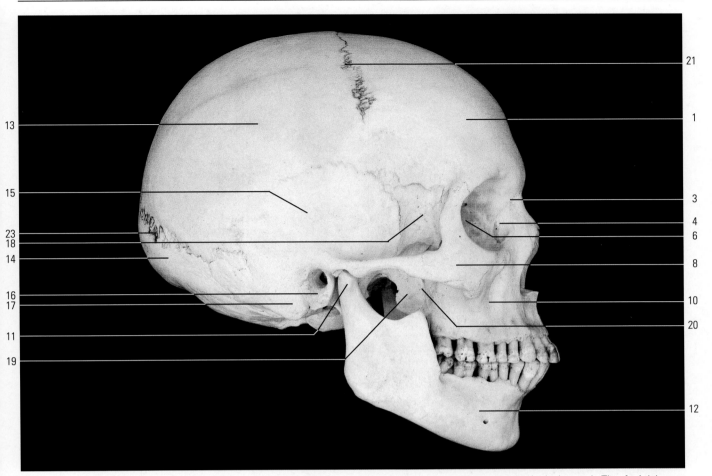

Human skull (lateral view). The cranial bones (neurocranium) cover the cranial cavity where the brain is located. The facial bones (viscerocranium) form the oral and nasal cavities as well as the two orbits. They lie above each other in one plane, thus forming the bony background for the human face. The **skull of the newborn** (figures below) is still growing. Sutures and fontanelles are the places where tissue growing and bone formation takes place. Note the small size of the facial bones, which do not reach their final gestalt before completed dentition.

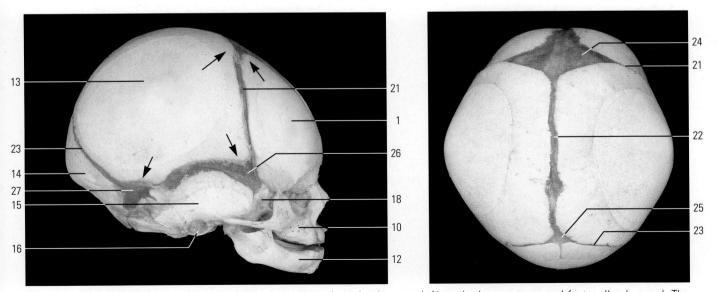

Skull of a newborn (left = lateral view, right = from above, frontal pole on top). Note the large sutures and fontanelles (arrows). The anterior fontanelle (24) has a rhomboid, the posterior (25) a triangular form. The two parts of the frontal bone fuse around the second year of life so that the frontal suture still discernible in the right photo eventually disappears.

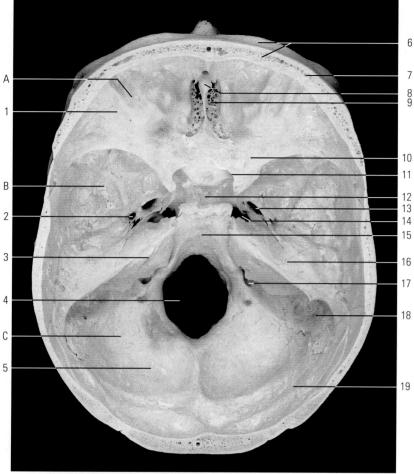

A = Anterior cranial fossa
(cerebrum, frontal lobe)
B = Middle cranial fossa
(cerebrum, temporal lobe)
C = Posterior cranial fossa
(cerebellum)

1 Orbital plate of frontal bone
(roof of orbit)
2 Foramen spinosum
(opening for middle meningeal vessels)
3 External acoustic meatus
4 Foramen magnum
5 **Occipital bone**
6 **Frontal bone**
7 Calvaria with diploe
8 Crista galli
9 **Lamina cribrosa** (openings for olfactory
nerves of nasal cavity)
10 Ala minor of sphenoid bone
11 Optic canal
12 **Sella turcica** of sphenoid bone
13 Foramen ovale
(opening for mandibular nerve, n. V$_3$)
14 Foramen lacerum
(opening for internal carotid artery)
15 Clivus
16 Petrous part of temporal bone
(contains the inner and middle ear)
12 Foramen jugulare (opening for cranial
nerves, n. IX, n. X, and n. XI)
18 Groove of sigmoid sinus
19 Groove of transverse sinus
20 **Frontal sinus**
21 Bony part of nasal septum
22 **Sphenoid sinus**
23 Vomer
24 Incisive canal
25 Hard palate
26 Mandible
27 **Parietal bone**
28 Grooves of middle meningeal artery
and vein
29 **Sphenoid bone**
30 Mandibular foramen
(entrance of mandibular canal)

Base of the skull (from above). The three cranial fossae (A, B, C) are not placed at the same level. The posterior cranial fossa (C) lies deeper than the middle (B) and anterior (A) fossa.

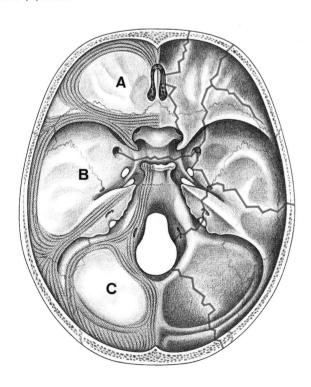

Base of the skull (from above). Left half of drawing: A, B, C = cranial fossae; red areas and lines = more compact bone structure. Right half of drawing = preferential sites of skull fractures.

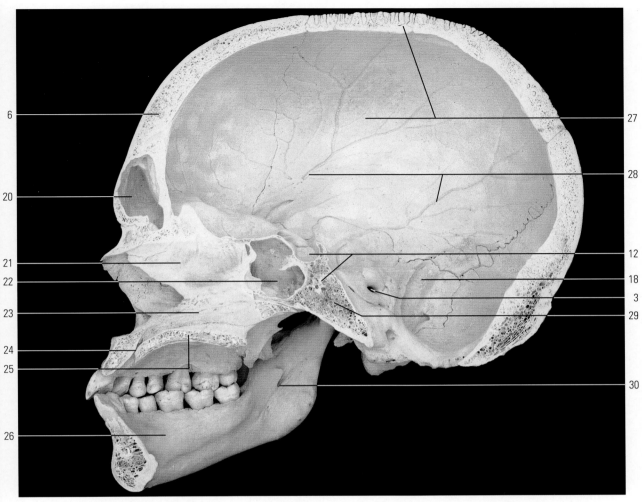

6
20
21
22
23
24
25
26

27
28
12
18
3
29
30

Sagittal section through the skull. The nasal septum (21) is still in place. Note the different level of the three cranial fossae and the location of the frontal (20) and sphenoid (22) sinus.

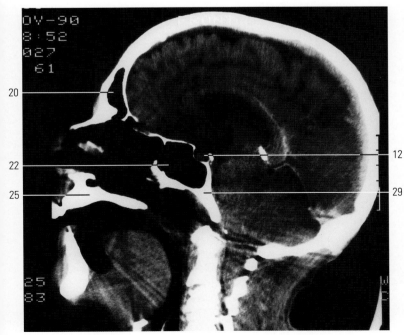

20
22
25

12
29

Sagittal section through the head (CT image) (compare with figure above).

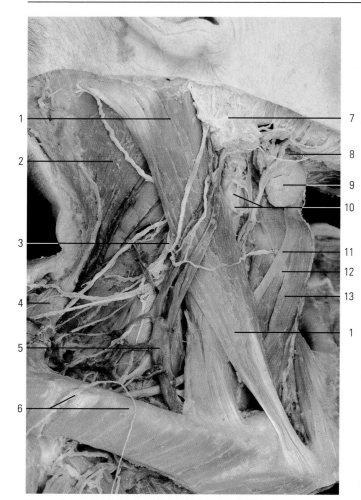

1
2
3
4
5
6

7
8
9
10
11
12
13
1

Lateral cervical region (superficial layer). The four great cutaneous nerves of the neck reach the subcutis in the middle of the posterior border of the sternocleidomastoid muscle (1) (so-called Erb's point) (3).

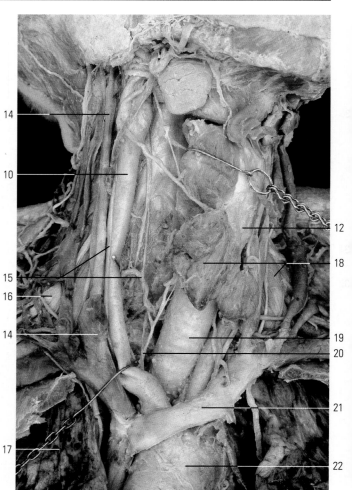

14
10
15
16
14
17

12
18
19
20
21
22

Deeper layer of lateral cervical region (right side, oblique-anterior view). Thyroid gland and common carotid artery have been reflected to display the inferior laryngeal recurrent nerve (20) innervating the intrinsic muscles of the larynx and the inferior thyroid artery (15).

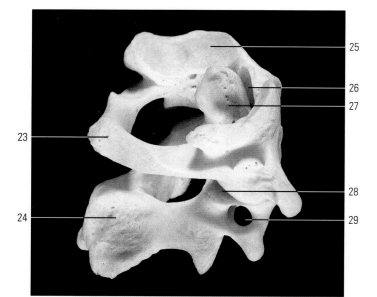

23
24

25
26
27
28
29

Atlas and axis (first and second cervical vertebrae, oblique lateral view from above). These two vertebrae support the head balanced on the upper articular surface of the atlas (25).

The **atlas, axis,** and occipital bone form six small joints responsible for the subtle movements of the head. The two atlanto-occipital joints allow minor movements of flexion and extension (e.g., nodding), the three atlanto-axial joints allow rotation of both, head and axis, as a unit. The **vertebral artery** lies deep inside the triangle formed by the respective muscle groups (see diagram on page 119). The vertebral artery travels along the cervical vertebra's transverse processes and reaches the base of the skull via the posterior arch of atlas (branches of vertebral and internal carotid artery together supply the brain).

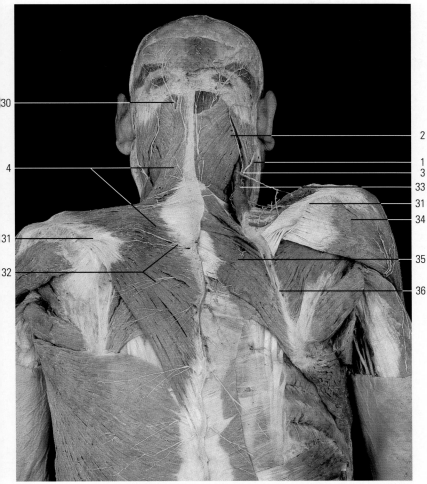

Muscles and nerves of the neck and back; left = superficial layer; right = deeper layer (here, the trapezius muscle has been removed).

1 Sternocleidomastoid muscle
2 Splenius capitis muscle
3 **Erb's point** (punctum nervosum)
4 **Trapezius muscle**
5 External jugular vein
6 Clavicle
7 Parotid gland
8 Facial artery
9 Submandibular gland
10 **Common carotid artery**
11 Omohyoid muscle
12 Location of larynx
13 Infrahyoid muscles
14 Internal jugular vein
15 Vagus nerve and inferior thyroid artery
16 **Brachial plexus**
17 Lung
18 **Thyroid gland**
19 Trachea
20 **Recurrent laryngeal nerve** (innervation of intrinsic laryngeal muscles)
21 Left brachiocephalic vein
22 Aortic arch
23 **Atlas** (first cervical vertebra)
24 **Axis** (second cervical vertebra)
25 Superior articular facet of atlas (for atlanto-occipital joint)
26 Location of median atlanto-axial joint
27 Dens of axis
28 Location of lateral atlanto-axial joint
29 Foramen transversarium (for vertebral artery and vein)
30 **Greater occipital nerve** (C_2)
31 Spine of scapula
32 Cutaneous nerves (branches of dorsal rami of spinal nerves)
33 Levator scapulae muscle
34 Deltoid muscle
35 Greater rhomboid muscle
36 Medial border of scapula
37 Greater and smaller rectus capitis posterior muscles
38 Superior and inferior obliquus capitis muscles
39 **Vertebral artery**
40 Occipital artery

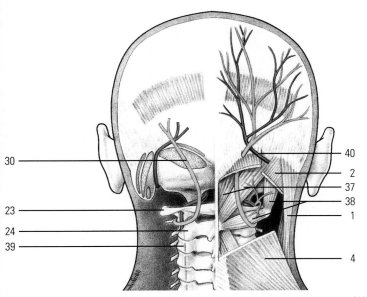

Deepest muscles of the neck in relation to greater occipital nerve (30). Note the course of vertebral (39) and occipital (40) arteries.

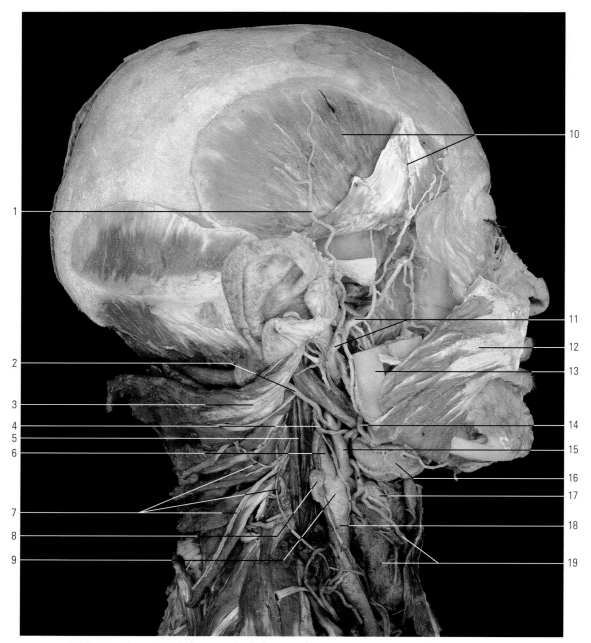

Arteries of the head and neck (lateral view). Ramus of mandible has been removed to show the maxillary artery (11). Temporalis (10), masseter (12), and sternocleidomastoid (3) muscles have been reflected. Note the location of the carotid sinus (9) where the common carotid artery divides into the internal carotid artery (6), which supplies the brain and the external carotid artery (15), which supplies the facial regions of the head.

1 **Superficial temporal artery**
2 Occipital artery
3 Sternocleidomastoid muscle (cut and reflected)
4 Hypoglossal nerve (n. XII)
5 Internal jugular vein
6 **Internal carotid artery**
7 Cutaneous branches of the cervical plexus
8 Lymph node
9 Division of common carotid artery into internal and external

carotid artery (carotid sinus)
10 Temporalis muscle
11 **Maxillary artery**
12 Masseter muscle (reflected)
13 Mandible
14 **Facial artery**
15 **External carotid artery**
16 Submandibular gland
17 Larynx
18 **Common carotid artery**

19 Thyroid gland and superior thyroid artery
20 Posterior cerebral artery
21 Cerebellar arteries
22 **Vertebral artery**
23 Anterior cerebral artery
24 Middle cerebral artery
25 Internal carotid artery at the base of skull (siphon of carotis)
26 Trapezius muscle

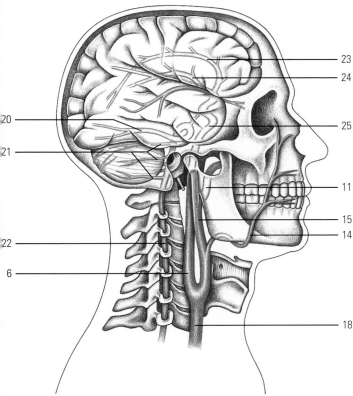

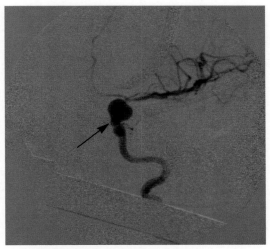

Arteriogram of the internal carotid artery.
Arrow = pathologic dilation (aneurysma) of the carotid artery at skull base.

Arteries of the brain (lateral view). The brain is supplied on either side by two great arteries: 1) the internal carotid artery (6), and 2) the vertebral artery (22).

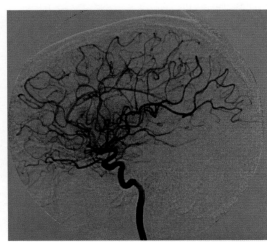

Arteriogram of internal carotid artery and its cerebral branches (X-ray image, lateral view, frontal pole of the brain to the left).

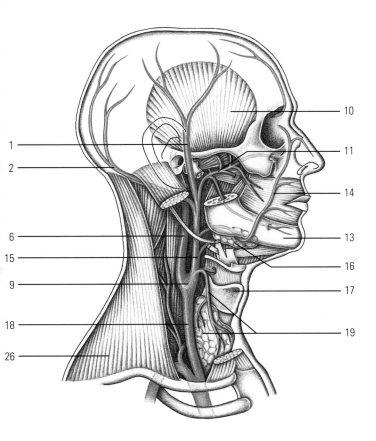

Cerebral arteries are branches of the **vertebral artery** (traveling within the cervical vertebral column and entering the cranial cavity through the foramen magnum) and the **internal carotid artery** (entering the cranial cavity through the carotid canal of the petrous part of the temporal bone).

◄
Arteries of the head and neck (schematic drawing). Lower jaw and sternocleidomastoid muscle are partially removed. The common carotid artery (9) is slightly enlarged where it divides into the internal (6) and external (15) carotid artery. The intercarotid body (carotid glomus), a sensory organ responsible for the regulation of blood pressure and respiration, is situated here.

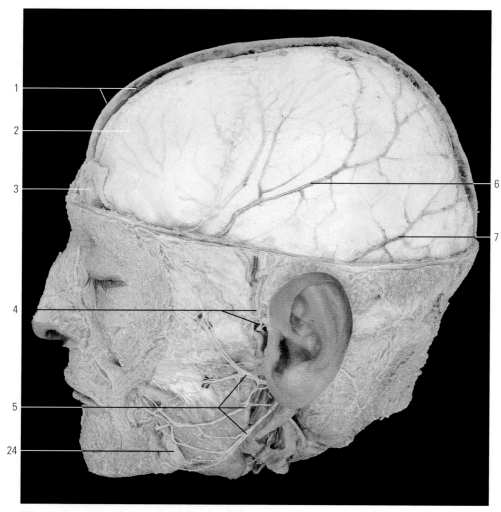

1 Calvaria and skin
2 **Dura mater**
3 Frontal sinus
4 Auriculotemporal nerve and superficial temporal artery and vein
5 **Facial nerve** (n. VII) (innervation of facial muscles)
6 Anterior branch of the middle meningeal artery
7 Posterior branch of the middle meningeal artery
8 **Middle meningeal artery**
9 Skin of the scalp
10 Galea aponeurotica
11 Calvaria and pericranium
12 **Arachnoidea** and **pia mater** with blood vessels
13 Brain with cerebral vessels
14 Sponge bone of the skull (diploe) with diploic veins
15 **Superior sagittal sinus**
16 **Subarachnoid space** (contains cerebrospinal fluid)
17 Falx cerebri
18 Meningeal blood vessels
19 Oculomotor nerve (n. III)
20 Sella turcica with pituitary gland
21 Tentorium of cerebellum
22 Optic nerve and internal carotid artery
23 Greater occipital nerve (C_2)
24 Facial vein
25 Parotid gland and branches of the facial nerve
26 Inferior sagittal sinus
27 Straight sinus
28 **Cavernous sinus**
29 Transverse sinus
30 Internal jugular vein
31 Pterygoid venous plexus

Dissection of the dura mater (2) with middle meningeal vessels (6, 7). The vessels lie between the dura and cranial bones (epidural location). A rupture of these vessels leads to epidural hematoma.

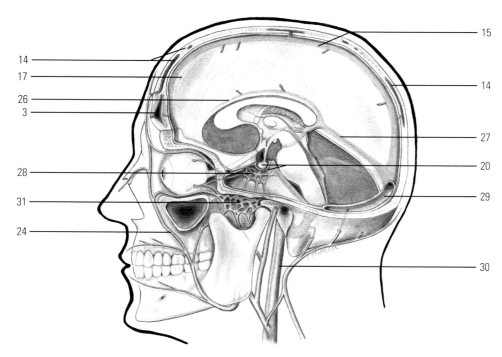

◄ **Veins of the head and neck** (lateral view). The sinuses of dura mater are incorporated within the dura and drained mainly into the internal jugular vein (30).

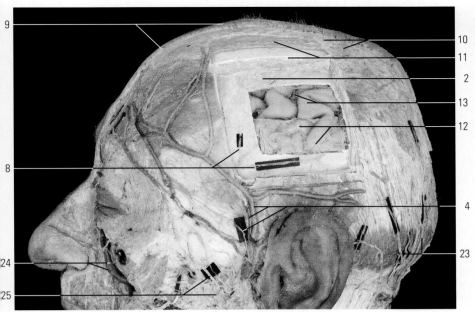

Protecting coverings of the brain

Layers from outward to inward:

1. Skin (9)
2. Galea aponeurotica (10)
3. Periosteum (pericranium) (11)
4. Bone (calvaria) (11)
5. **Dura mater** (2) with meningeal vessels (8)
6. Arachnoidea with subarachnoidal space (12)
7. Pia mater (12)
8. **Brain** with cerebral vessels (13)

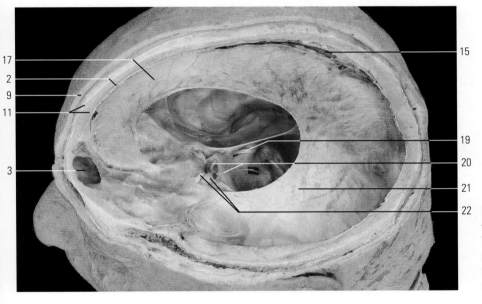

Organization of the dura mater within the cranial cavity (from above). The brain has been removed. The cerebellum is situated underneath the tentorium (21), i.e., within the infratentorial space.

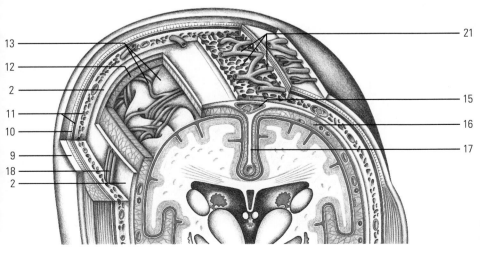

Protecting coverings of the brain (meninges and layers of the skull) (schematic drawing).

1 Frontal lobe of left
   hemisphere
2 Orbicularis oculi muscle
3 Facial nerve (n. VII)
4 Parietal lobe of left
   hemisphere
5 **Central sulcus** (border
   between frontal and
   parietal lobe)
6 **Lateral sulcus** of Sylvius
7 Occipital lobe
8 Temporal lobe
9 Tentorium of cerebellum
   (located between
   cerebellum and cerebrum)
10 **Cerebellum**
11 **Precentral gyrus**
   (somatomotor area of brain)
12 **Postcentral gyrus** (somato-
   sensory area of brain)
13 Area 19
   (tertiary visual center)
14 **Area calcarina** (area 17)
   (primary visual center)
15 Area 18
   (secondary visual center)
16 **Primary auditive center**
   (Heschl's gyri)
17 Secondary auditive centers
18 Tertiary auditive centers
   (sensory speech area of
   Wernicke)
19 Insular lobe

Location of the brain within the cranial cavity (lateral view). The cerebellum (10) lies underneath the tentorium (9). Note the location of the central (5) and lateral (6) sulcus, borders of the brain lobes.

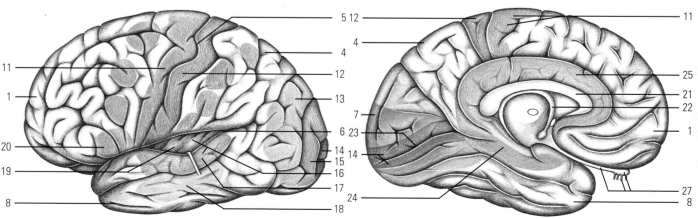

Cortical areas of the left hemisphere (lateral view, insular lobe is shown, frontal pole to the left).

Cortical areas of the left hemisphere (medial view, brain stem removed).

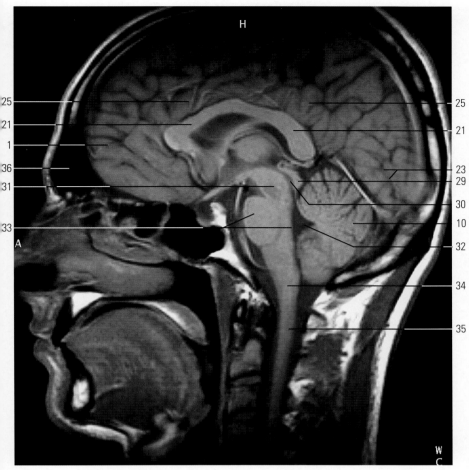

20 Motor speech area of Broca
21 Corpus callosum
22 Fornix
23 Calcarine sulcus
24 Hippocampus
   (part of the limbic system)
25 Cingulum
26 **Optic nerve** (n. II)
27 Olfactory fila, olfactory bulb
   and tract
28 Pineal body
29 **Colliculi of the midbrain**
30 **Cerebral aqueduct** (connection
   between third and fourth
   ventricle)
31 Brainstem
32 Fourth ventricle
33 Pons and rhomboid fossa
34 Medulla oblongata
35 Spinal cord (medulla spinalis)
36 Frontal sinus

Sagittal section through the head (MR image). Note the location of the brain within the cranial cavity.

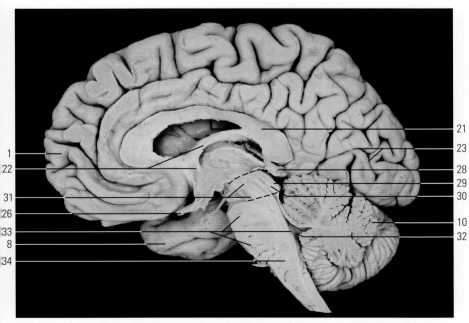

Right half of the brain and brain stem. Frontal pole to the left. Dotted lines mark the location of the midbrain.

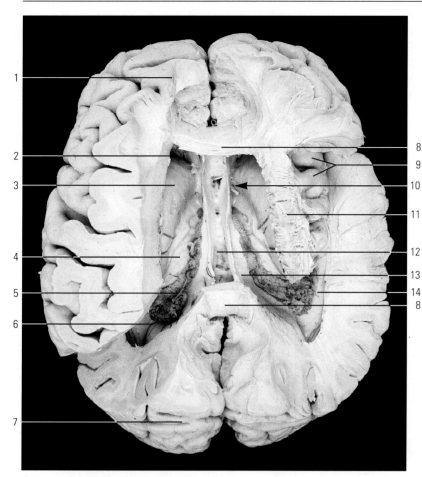

1 Frontal lobe
2 Anterior horn of the lateral ventricle
3 **Caudate nucleus**
4 **Thalamus** (part of diencephalon)
5 **Choroid plexus**
6 Posterior horn of the lateral ventricle
7 Occipital lobe
8 Corpus callosum
9 Insular lobe
10 Interventricular foramen of Monro
   (connection between lateral and third
   ventricle)
11 **Internal capsule**
12 Roof of the third ventricle
13 Fornix (part of limbic system)
14 **Hippocampus**
15 Pituitary gland
16 Pons
17 Short association fibers
18 Projection fibers within the internal capsule
19 Interthalamic adhesion
20 Cerebellum
21 Medulla oblongata
22 Septum pellucidum
23 **Third ventricle** (region of diencephalon)
24 **Pineal body**
25 **Colliculi of midbrain**
26 Rhomboid fossa
   (at the bottom of 4th ventricle)
27 Cerebellar peduncles
28 Vestibulocochlear nerve (n. VIII)
29 Cerebral aqueduct (Sylvius' canal)

Lateral ventricles of the brain (from above). Parts of the cerebral cortex and corpus callosum have been removed and the lateral ventricle (2, 6) on both sides opened. Choroid plexus (5) protruding into the ventricle can be seen.

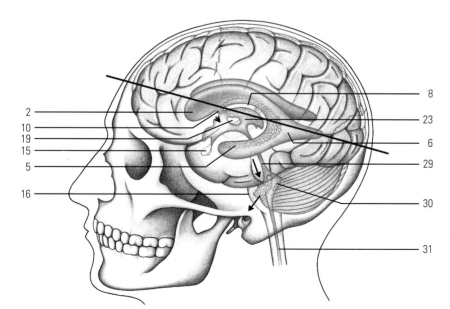

Location of the brain ventricles (2, 6) (lateral view). Choroid plexus (5), site of cerebrospinal fluid production is indicated in red. Arrows = direction of flow. Black line = plane of horizontal sections, shown on opposite page.

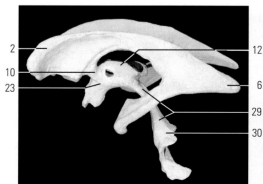

Corrosion cast of ventricles of the brain (lateral view, frontal pole to the left).

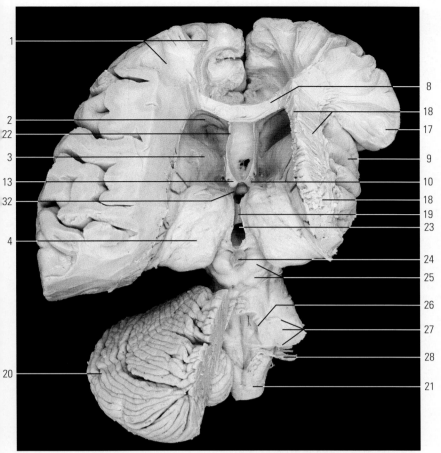

30 Fourth ventricle (possesses three openings into the surrounding subarachnoid space: the two lateral apertures of Luschka and the median aperture of Magendie)
31 Central canal of spinal cord
32 Anterior commissure

The **ventricles of the brain** contain a cell-free liquid (**cerebrospinal fluid**, CSF) produced in the choroid plexus (5). It flows from the lateral ventricles (2, 6) through the interventricular foramen of Monro (10) into the unpaired third ventricle continuing its flow through the cerebral aqueduct of Sylvius (29) into the fourth ventricle from where it enters the subarachnoidal space via three openings (30). Thus the brain is completely suspended in the CSF. The pacchionian bodies channel the fluid from the subarachnoidal space back into the **sinuses of dura mater**. Substances circulating in the blood can not enter the brain unhindered (blood-brain barrier). Numerous substances are also prevented from entering the CSF (blood-CSF-barrier). Those two barriers protect the brain from harmful substances.

Dissection of the basal ganglia of the brain (from above). Right half of the cerebellum and great portions of the cerebral cortex have been removed to display the caudate nucleus (3), the thalamus (4), and the rhomboid fossa (26).

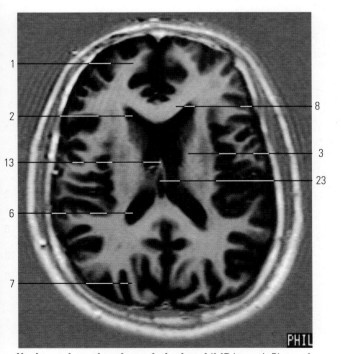

Horizontal section through the head (MR image). Plane of section see drawing on page 126.

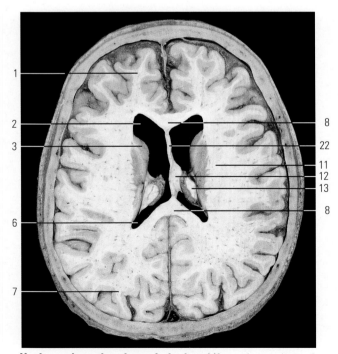

Horizontal section through the head (from above, plane of section see page 126).

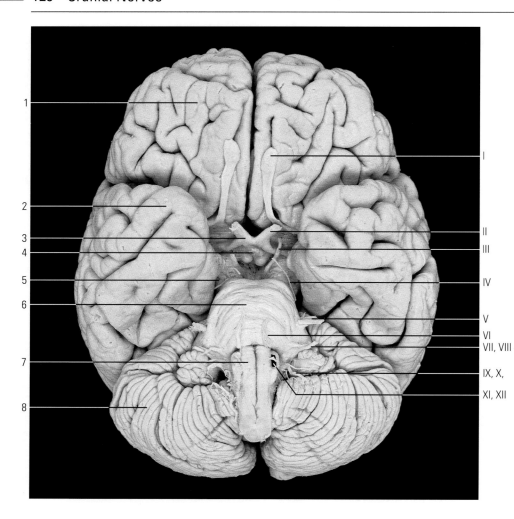

Brain with cranial nerves (from below). Note the location of the 12 cranial nerves leaving the brain stem.

1 Frontal lobe of cerebrum
2 Temporal lobe
3 **Optic chiasma**
4 Stalk of pituitary gland (infundibulum)
5 Cerebral peduncle
6 Pons
7 Pyramid
8 Cerebellum
9 Superior rectus muscle of eye
10 Inferior rectus muscle of eye
11 Buccal nerve
12 Lingual nerve
13 **Inferior alveolar nerve** (branch of mandibular nerve, n. V$_3$)
14 Thalamus (part of diencephalon)
15 Colliculi of midbrain
16 Rhomboid fossa
17 Anterior cranial fossa
18 Middle cranial fossa
19 Petrous part of temporal bone
20 Internal acoustic meatus
21 Posterior cranial fossa
22 Throat (pharynx)
23 Sympathetic trunk with superior cervical ganglion
24 Common carotid artery dividing in internal and external carotid artery)
25 Superior dental plexus
26 Inferior dental plexus
27 Internal carotid artery

Cranial nerves (n. = nerve)	Related structures and functions
I Olfactory n.	Olfaction, olfactory mucous membrane
II Optic n.	Eyeball, seeing
III Oculomotor n.	Motor innervation of four extrinsic eye muscles, parasympathetic innervation of ciliary muscle and iris sphincter
IV Trochlear n.	Motor innervation of superior oblique muscle
V Trigeminal n	
V$_1$ Ophthalmic n.	Sensory innervation of eye and orbit
V$_2$ Maxillary n.	Sensory innervation of maxillary region and teeth
V$_3$ Mandibular n.	Innervation of mandibular region, teeth, muscles of mastication
VI Abducent n.	Motor innervation of lateral rectus muscle
VII Facial n.	Motor innervation of facial muscles
VIII Vestibulocochlear n.	Ear, vestibular apparatus, hearing, regulation of equilibrium and posture
IX Glossopharyngeal n.	Gustatory perceptions, innervation of pharyngeal muscle and parotid gland
X Vagus n.	Parasympathetic innervation of heart, lung, and gastrointestinal tract, innervation of larynx
XI Accessorius n.	Motor innervation of trapezius and sternocleidomastoid muscles
XII Hypoglossus n.	Motor innervation of tongue muscles

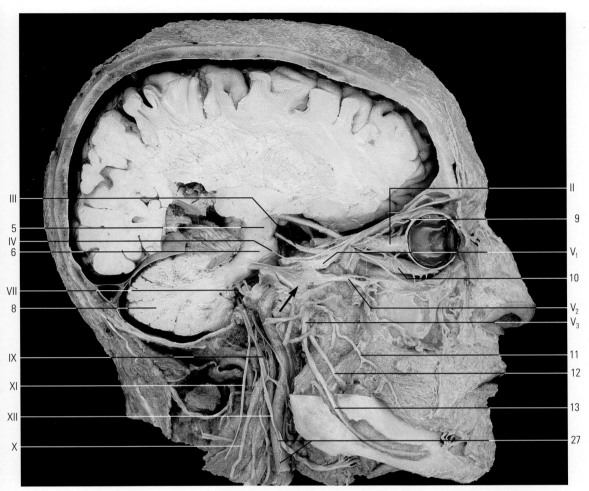

III
5
IV
6
VII
8
IX
XI
XII
X

II
9
V₁
10
V₂
V₃
11
12
13
27

Brain with cranial nerves (lateral view). Note particularly the three main branches of the trigeminal nerve (n. V) and their areas of innervation. They derive from the trigeminal ganglion (arrow).

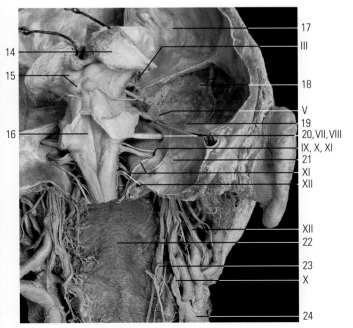

14
15
16

17
III
18
V
19
20, VII, VIII
IX, X, XI
21
XI
XII
XII
22
23
X
24

Brainstem with cranial nerves at the base of the skull (posterior view).

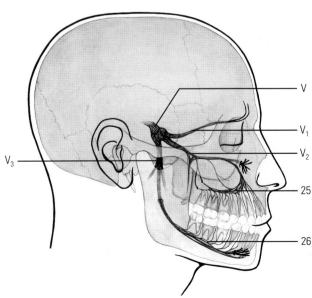

V
V₁
V₂
V₃
25
26

Ramification of trigeminal nerve (n. V) (lateral view). V₁, V₂, and V₃ = the three main branches of n. V (see table on page 128).

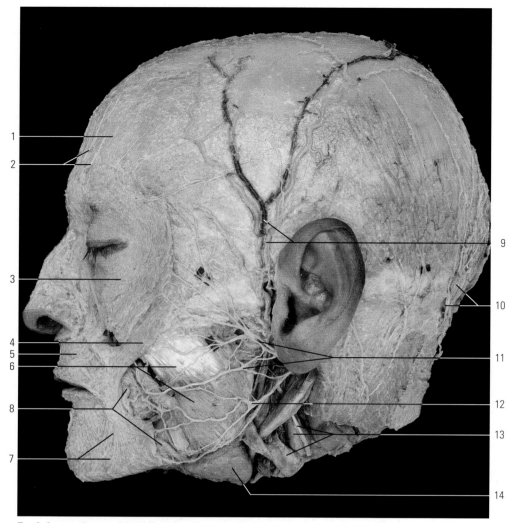

1 Occipitofrontalis muscle
2 Supraorbital nerves
3 Orbicularis oculi muscle
4 Zygomaticus major muscle
5 Orbicularis oris muscle
6 Masseter muscle
7 Depressor anguli oris muscle
8 Facial artery and vein
9 Auriculotemporalis nerve and superficial temporal artery and vein
10 Occipitalis major nerve (C_2)
11 Temporal branches of facial nerve
12 Buccal and zygomatic branches of facial nerve
13 Internal jugular vein and vagus nerve
14 Submandibular gland
15 Facial nerve
16 Platysma
17 Eyeball (bulbus oculi)
18 Optic nerve (n. II), ciliary nerves and ciliary ganglion
19 Lateral rectus muscle and abducent nerve (n. VI) (reflected)

Facial muscles and facial nerve (lateral view). The facial nerve (n. VII) leaves the skull through the stylomastoid foramen (not visible underneath the outer ear) and enters the parotid gland (removed), where it forms a plexus. The motor innervation of the facial muscles comes from branches of the facial nerve.

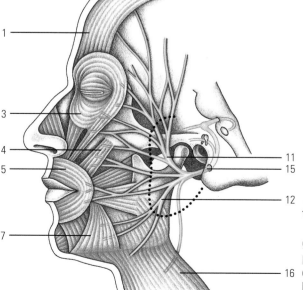

Facial muscles and course of the facial nerve (n. VII) (schematic drawing). Dotted line = border of parotid gland. Note the radially oriented pattern of the facial nerve branches entering the facial muscles from below.

Eye-muscle paralysis results in malpositions of the eye (squinting). When the abducent nerve is damaged, the eyeball can no longer move laterally (abducted), which results in convergent strabismus. Besides somatomotor fibers the oculomotor nerve also contains autonomic (parasympathetic) nerve fibers leading to the intrinsic eye muscles (ciliary muscle, sphincter muscle of pupil). Lesions of the oculomotor nerve can thus also result in a disorder of accommodation and pupillomotoricity.

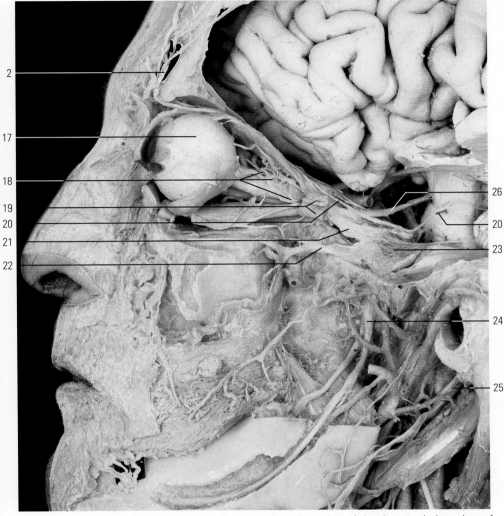

20 Trochlear nerve (n. IV)
21 Ophthalmic nerve (first branch of trigeminal nerve, n. V₁)
22 Maxillary nerve (second branch of trigeminal nerve, n. V₂)
23 Trigeminal ganglion of Gasser
24 Mandibular nerve (third branch of trigeminal nerve, n. V₃)
25 Facial nerve (n. VII)
26 Oculomotor nerve (N. VI)
27 Glossopharyngeal nerve (n. IX)
28 Vagus nerve (n. X)
29 Abducens nerve (n. VI)

Nerves innervating eye and extraocular muscles, dissection of the three main branches of the trigeminal nerve deriving from the trigeminal ganglion (23) (lateral view). Part of the mandible has been removed to show the mandibular branch of n. V (24), the inferior alveolar branch of which enters the mandibular canal and innervates the teeth.

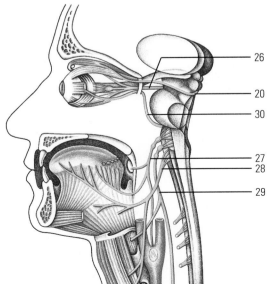

Location and course of cranial nerves innervating the eye and eye muscles, tongue, pharynx, supra- and infrahyoid muscles, and larynx.

The **facial nerve** is the somato-motor nerve for the facial or mimic muscles. Accompanied by the vestibulocochlear nerve, it enters the petrosal bone by the internal acoustic meatus and travels along the fallopian canal underneath the mucous membrane of the middle ear. The facial nerve then emerges from the stylomastoid foramen, branching off in the parotid gland. Damage to the facial nerve results in paralysis of the facial muscles (drooping angle of mouth, eyelids etc.) and facial disfigurements. Acoustic disorders like acoustic hyperesthesia (the patient experiences every sound painfully loud) may also appear. Peripheral facial paralysis affects all facial muscles, central facial paralysis excludes the muscles of the forehead and eyelids (frowning is still possible).

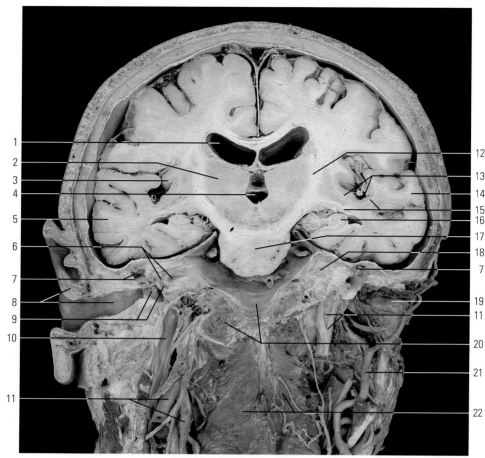

1 Lateral ventricle of the brain
2 Thalamus (diencephalon)
3 Insular lobe
4 Third ventricle
5 Temporal lobe of the brain
6 **Inner ear, cochlea and internal acoustic meatus**
7 **Tympanic cavity with auditory ossicles**
8 External acoustic meatus and auricle
9 Tympanic membrane and lateral semicircular canal
10 Internal jugular vein
11 Internal carotid artery and sympathetic trunk
12 Internal capsule
13 **Transverse temporal gyri of Heschl** (location of primary auditory area)
14 **Superior temporal gyrus** (location of auditory association area)
15 Acoustic radiation
16 Hippocampus (part of limbic system)
17 Brainstem
18 Petrous part of the temporal bone
19 Temporomandibular joint and head of mandible
20 Base of skull
21 Maxillary artery
22 Constrictor muscle of pharynx
23 **Vestibulocochlear nerve** (n. VIII)
24 Facial nerve (n. VII)
25 Internal acoustic meatus
26 **Cochlea**
27 **Superior semicircular duct**
28 Ampullae of semicircular ducts
29 Posterior semicircular duct
30 Lateral semicircular duct
31 Endolymphatic duct and sac
32 Medial geniculate body
33 **Lateral lemniscus** – part of the acoustic pathway
34 Cerebellum
35 Rhomboid fossa
36 Facial canal
37 Groove of the sigmoid sinus
38 Cast of internal carotid artery
39 Groove for middle meningeal artery and vein
40 Vertebral artery
41 Vestibulum with utriculus and sacculus

Cross section through the head at the level of the ear (from behind). On the left side the petrous part of the temporal bone is longitudinally sectioned so that outer, middle and inner ear (6, 7, 8) can be recognized. Note the fixation of pharynx (22) at the skull base (20).

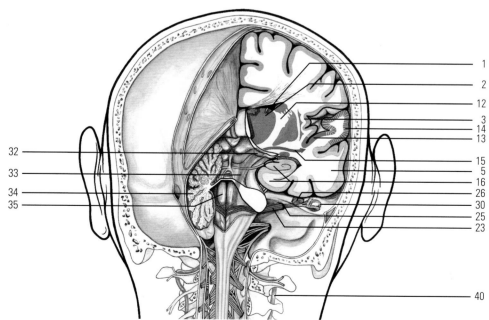

Auditory pathways in the brain (schematic drawing). Sound messages from the inner ear (Corti's organ of cochlea) are transported by the vestibulocochlear nerve (n. VIII) (23) to nuclei of the rhomboid fossa (35). From here, they reach the auditory areas in the temporal lobe (13, 14) by way of lateral lemniscus (33) and medial geniculate body (32).

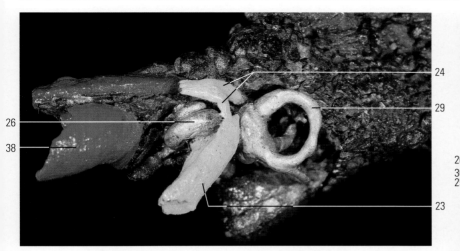

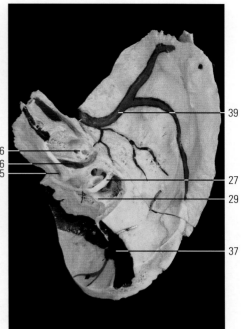

Corrosion cast of the inner ear (right side, from behind). Cochlea, vestibulum, and semicircular ducts are filled with Wood's metal. Vestibulocochlear (23) and facial (24) nerves are colored in yellow, the internal carotid artery in red (38).

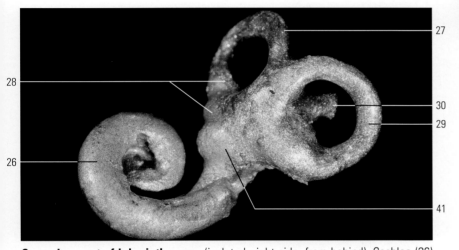

Right temporal bone (from above). Preparation of semicircular ducts (27, 29) and cochlea (26). Blue = groove for sigmoid sinus; red = groove for middle meningeal artery (39); yellow = facial canal.

Corrosion cast of labyrinth organ (isolated, right side, from behind). Cochlea (26) and semicircular ducts (27, 29, 30) are connected with each other by the vestibulum (41).

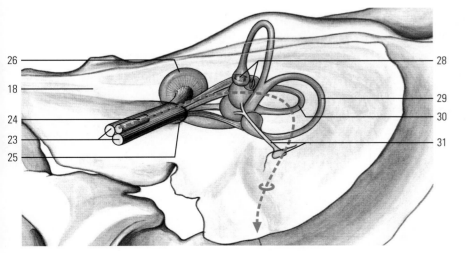

Location of labyrinth organ within the petrous part of the temporal bone (right side, from behind). Dotted line (red) = course of the facial nerve (24).

The **cochlea** (26) contains sensory hair cells needed for the perception of sound. Nervous stimulation is transmitted to the temporal lobe of the brain via the medial geniculate body part of the diencephalon (auditory pathway). The primary auditory brain centers serve acoustic perception; the secondary and tertiary centers process acoustic understanding and memory (linguistic and articulate sense, musicalness etc.).

The **facial nerve** (24), accompanied by the vestibulocochlear nerve (n. VIII) extends into the inner ear. It travels right underneath the mucous membrane of the middle ear inferior to the lateral semicircular duct from where it leaves the base of the skull through the stylomastoid foramen. The facial nerve is prone to injuries resulting from skull fractures and inflammations of the middle ear. Damage to the facial nerve can result in hearing and balance disorders as well as paralysis of the facial muscles.

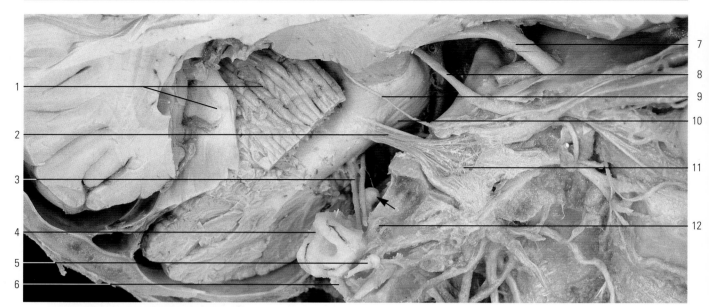

Cranial nerves deriving from the brain stem and vestibular organ, dissected from the skull (lateral view). The three semicircular ducts (4) have been opened and the outer ear removed. The auditory ossicles (5) remained in place. Arrow = small tumor (neurinoma) within the vestibulocochlear nerve (3). Note the location of the trigeminal ganglion (11).

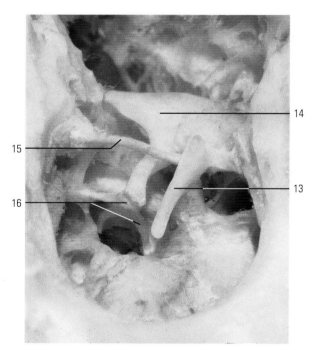

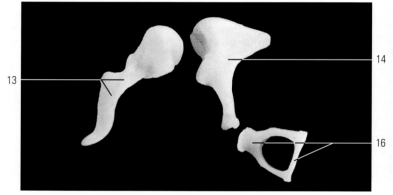

Auditory ossicles (isolated from the right tympanic cavity).

Auditory ossicles within the tympanic cavity (right side, lateral view, tympanic membrane has been removed).

Receptors for equilibrium. The vestibular apparatus consists of the utriculus and saccule in the vestibule (19) and three semicircular ducts (4) filled by endolymph (red in the diagram). The **utricle** and **saccule** function in static equilibrium, while the semicircular ducts are concerned with dynamic (kinetic) equilibrium. The three **semicircular ducts** project from the vestibule at approximately right angles to each other. Each duct possesses an ampulla with a cupula. If the cupula is bent, the sensory hair cells are distorted leading to the nervous stimulation.

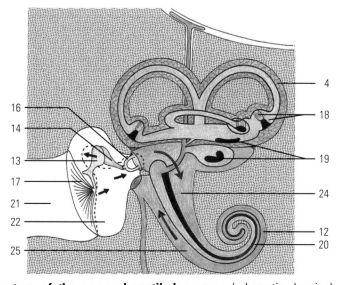

Structure of the ear and vestibular organ (schematic drawing). Arrows = direction of movements; green = perilymph; red = endolymph; black = sensory organs.

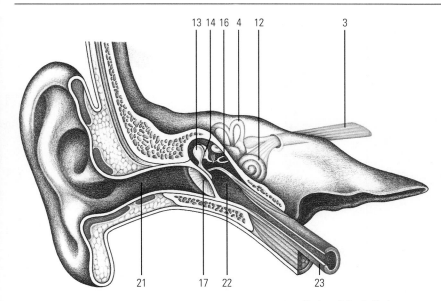

1 Cerebellum and tentorium cerebelli
2 **Trigeminal nerve** (n. V)
3 **Vestibulocochlear nerve** (n. VIII)
4 Semicircular ducts
5 Auditory ossicles within the tympanic cavity
6 Facial nerve (n. VII)
7 Optic tract
8 Oculomotor nerve (n. III)
9 Trochlear nerve (n. IV)
10 Brainstem
11 Trigeminal ganglion
12 **Cochlea**
13 **Malleus**
14 **Incus**
15 Chorda tympani (branch of facial nerve)
16 Stapes
17 **Tympanic membrane**
18 Ampulla of semicircular duct
19 Maculae staticae
20 **Ductus cochlearis** with Corti's organ
21 External acoustic meatus
22 **Tympanic cavity**
23 Auditory tube (eustachian tube)
24 Scala vestibuli
25 Scala tympani
26 Tectorial membrane
27 Corti's organ with sensory hair cells
28 Basilar membrane
29 Cochlear nerves
30 Spiral ganglion (nerve cells for auditory pathway)
31 Scala vestibuli and Reissner's membrane

Structure of the auditory organ. Three parts have to be distinguished: 1) the external ear and auditory meatus (21), ending at the tympanic membrane (17); 2) the middle ear with three auditory ossicles, connected with the pharynx by the auditory or eustachian tube (23); and 3) the inner ear (cochlea, 12) embedded within the petrous part of the temporal bone.

The hearing process. Sound waves initiate vibrations of the tympanic membrane (17) and the auditory ossicles (13, 14, 16). The stapes (16) transmit the vibrations to the oval window and perilymph of the scala vestibuli (24). The perilymph oscillations in turn are then transferred to the cochlear duct (20), where the tectorial membrane (26) mechanically stimulates the sensory cells in the Corti's organ (27). The cochlear part of the vestibulocochlear nerve (n. VIII) (3) transmits this stimulation to the acoustic centers of the brain (auditory pathway).

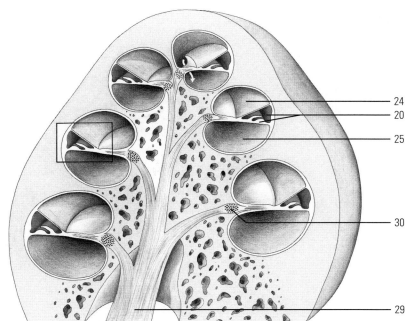

Structure of the cochlea. The section shows the cochlear duct with Corti's organ (20), filled with endolymph (red) and the perilymph containing two surrounding scalae [vestibular (24) and tympanic (25) scala].

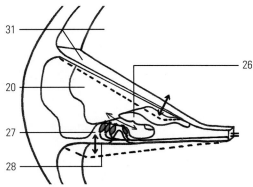

Movements of the cochlear duct (arrows), the prerequisite for auditory perception. Red = sensory cells (hair cells).

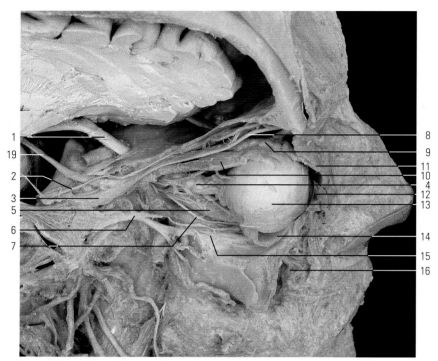

1 Optic tract
2 **Trochlear nerve** (n. IV)
3 Ophthalmic nerve (n. V$_1$)
4 **Optic nerve** (n. II)
5 **Inferior rectus muscle** of eye
6 Maxillary nerve (n. V$_2$)
7 Inferior branch of oculomotorius nerve (n. III)
8 Frontal nerve (branch of n. V$_1$)
9 Levator palpebrae superior muscle
10 **Superior rectus muscle** of eye
11 Upper eyelid
12 Cornea
13 Sclera
14 **Inferior obliquus muscle** of eye
15 Infraorbital nerve (branch of n. V$_2$)
16 Nasal and labial branches of infraorbital nerve
17 **Superior obliquus muscle** of eye
18 **Lateral rectus muscle** of eye
19 Oculomotor nerve (n. III)
20 **Trigeminal ganglion** of Gasser
21 **Lacrimal gland**
22 Orbicularis oculi muscle
23 Schlemm's canal
24 Trabecular meshwork (site of aqueous outflow)
25 **Ciliary muscle**
26 Ciliary processes (site of aqueous humor production)
27 Iris
28 Lens
29 Zonula apparatus (fixation of lens)
30 Lacrimal ducts
31 Lacrimal sac
32 Nasolacrimal duct

Eye within the orbit showing the extrinsic eye muscles and the related nerves (right eye, lateral view).

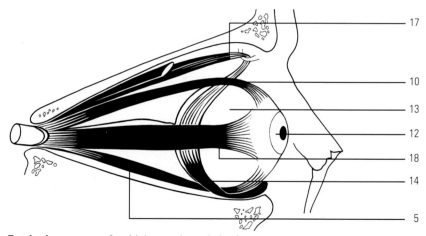

Extrinsic eye muscles (right eye, lateral view).

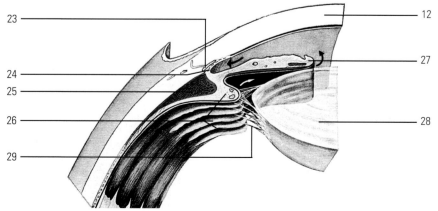

Accommodation apparatus and aqueous humor circulation system (arrow = direction of flow; red = ciliary muscle).

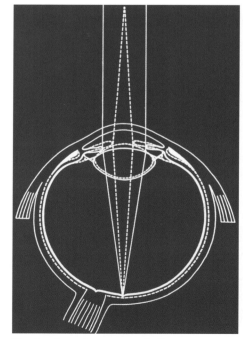

Mechanism of accommodation

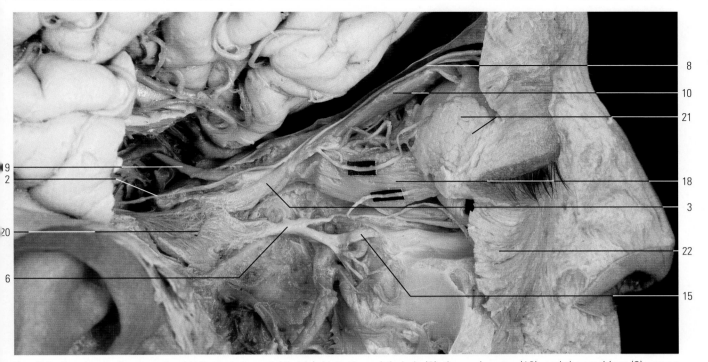

Eye lids, lacrimal gland, and orbit (lateral view, right side). Note the ophthalmic (3), the oculomotor (19), and the trochlear (2) nerves entering the orbit.

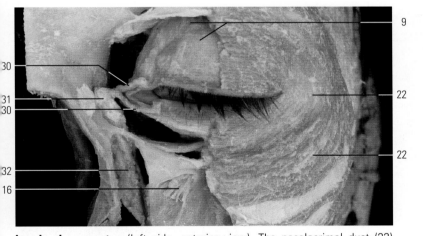

Lacrimal apparatus (left side, anterior view). The nasolacrimal duct (32) opens under the inferior nasal concha.

Extrinsic eye muscles		
(innervation and function)		
Lateral rectus	N. VI	Abduction
Medial rectus	N. III	Adduction
Superior rectus	N. III	Adduction, elevation, intortion
Inferior rectus	N. III	Adduction, depression, extortion
Superior oblique	N. IV	Abduction, depression, intortion
Inferior oblique	N. III	Abduction, elevation, extortion

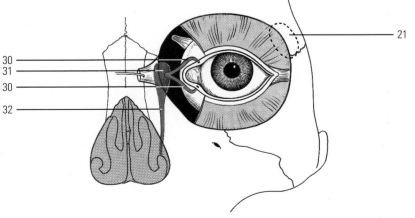

Lacrimal apparatus (shown in red). Dotted line = location of the lacrimal gland (21).

Visual accommodation (the ability to focus in close vision) is achieved by contraction of the ciliary muscle and relaxation of the zonular fibers which increases the curvature of the lens and thereby its refractive power. Simultaneously, the sphincter muscle of the iris contracts so that the pupil becomes smaller (miosis).

Aqueous humor circulation. The intraocular fluid is produced in the ciliary processes. It supplies the lens and flows into the anterior chamber of the eye via the pupil. From there the fluid continues its flow through the trabecular meshwork of the chamber angle into Schlemm's canal and further into the intra- and episcleral veins. If the aqueous outflow is blocked, intraocular pressure (normally 15–18 mmHg) can rise (glaucoma).

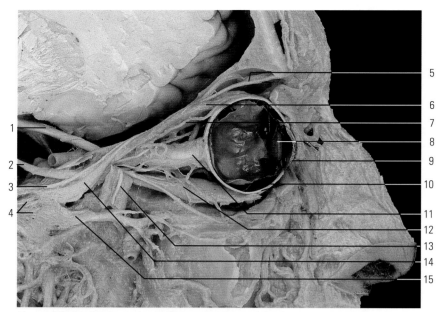

1 Optic tract
2 Oculomotor nerve (n. III)
3 Trochlear nerve (n. IV)
4 Trigeminal nerve (n. V) and
   trigeminal ganglion of Gasser
5 Frontal nerve
6 Superior rectus muscle of eye
7 **Ophthalmic artery**
8 Lens
9 Cornea
10 Sclera and retina
11 **Optic nerve** (n. II)
12 Inferior rectus muscle of eye
13 Lateral rectus muscle of eye and
   abducent nerve (n. VI)
14 Ophthalmic nerve (n. V_1)
   (first branch of trigeminal nerve)
15 Maxillary nerve (n. V_2)
   (second branch of trigeminal nerve)
16 Orbicularis oculi muscle
17 Levator palpebrae superioris muscle
   (for elevation of upper eyelid)
18 Tarsalis superior muscle
19 **Conjunctiva**
20 Iris
21 Ciliary body and zonular apparatus
   (for fixation of lens)
22 Central retina artery and vein
23 Vitreous body
24 Optic nerve head
25 Nerve fiber layer of retina
26 Ganglion cell layer of retina
   (3rd neuron)
27 Inner nuclear layer
   (containing bipolar cells, 2nd neuron)
28 Outer nuclear layer [comprising
   photoreceptor cells (rods and cones),
   1st neuron]
29 Retinal pigment epithelium
   (for nutrition and regeneration
   of photoreceptor cells)
30 Choroid
   (consisting of blood vessels)
31 Sclera

Eye with extrinsic eye muscles within the orbit (right side, lateral view); eye and lids were cut in half. The rectus lateralis muscle has been cut and reflected to display the related abducent nerve (13).

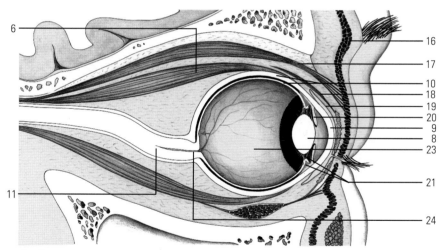

Sagittal section through eye, lids, and orbit with extrinsic eye muscles.
Arrow = location of the fovea centralis; red line = conjunctiva (19).

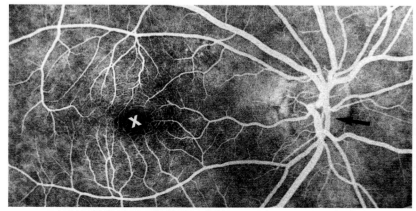

Fluorescent angiogram of retina vessels. x = location of fovea centralis; arrow = optic nerve disc (courtesy of Prof. Okamura, Kumamoto/Japan).

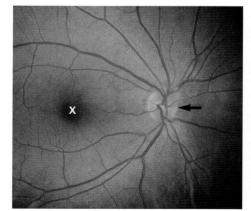

Ocular fundus showing the fovea centralis (x), optic disc (arrow), and retina vessels.

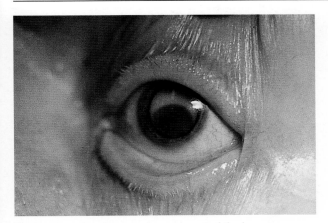

Human eye showing a nuclear cataract of the lens.

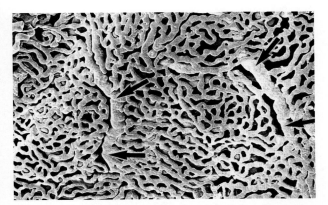

Corrosion cast of blood vessels underlying the retina (scanning electron micrograph of choriocapillaris, arrows = veins).

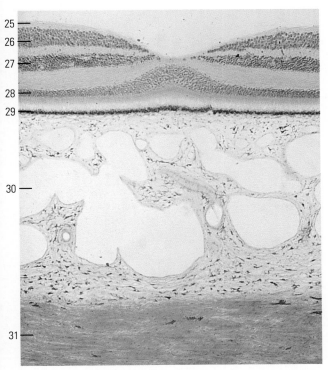

Light micrograph of the retina with the adjacent choroid and sclera, showing the fovea centralis.

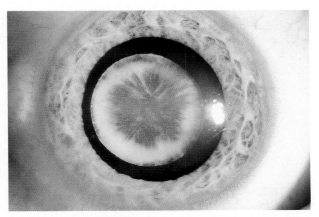

Anterior eye segment. The iris has been dilated with atropine so the lens with its senile cataract became visible in its entirety.

The **retina** contains two kinds of sensory cells: rods responsible for the light-dark adjustment and cones responsible for the perception of colors (blue, red, and green). The rods and cones are turned outwards (away from the entrance of light), facing the retinal pigmented epithelium and the choroid. The internal layers of the retina contain numerous transmitter neurons (bipolar cells, optic nerve cells) and retinal vessels. In the area of the fovea centralis, the point of sharpest vision, the inner layers are shifted laterally so that light can directly reach the photoreceptor cells. The central fovea contains only cones.

Layers of the eyeball	
Tunica externa (external layer)	Cornea, sclera
Tunica media (uvea) (middle layer)	Iris, ciliary body, choroid
Tunica interna (internal layer)	Pigmented epithelium, retina

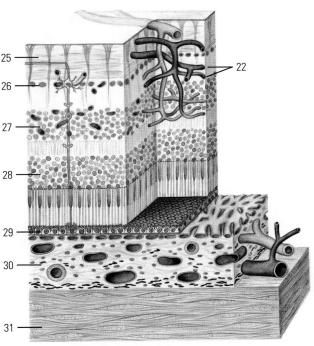

Structure of the retina and of the adjacent layers. Red = three retinal neurons transmitting light perception.

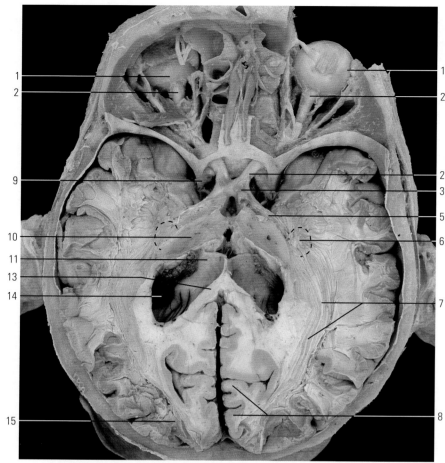

1 Eyeball (bulbus oculi)
2 **Optic nerve** (n. II)
3 **Optic chiasma**
4 Oculomotor nerve (n. III)
5 Optic tract
6 **Lateral geniculate body**
7 **Optic radiation of Gratiolet**
8 **Area calcarina**
  (primary visual area)
9 Internal carotid artery
10 Thalamus (part of diencephalon)
11 Crus of fornix
12 Colliculi of the midbrain
13 Corpus callosum
14 Inferior horn of the lateral ventricle
15 Occipital lobe
16 Visual field
17 **Retina**
18 Visual association areas
19 Ciliary ganglion
20 Ciliary nerves (innervation of
   ciliary muscle and iris sphincter)

Dissection of the eyes and visual pathway (from above). The two optic nerves (2) join each other in the optic chiasma (3). The optic tract (5) ends in the lateral geniculate body (6), from where the optic radiation (7) originates, transmitting visual sensations to the visual brain centers in the occipital lobe (8).

Injuries in the visual pathway
A Optic nerve – Complete blindness
B Optic chiasma – Partial blindness in both eyes
C Optic tract – Half of the visual field is lost (hemianopsy)
D Visual cortex – Cortical blindness
E Secondary visual areas – Deficiency in visual memory

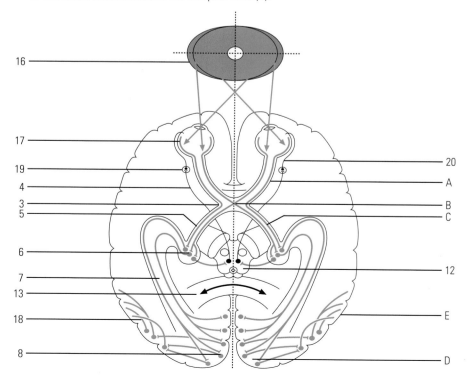

Visual pathway. Axons of retinal ganglion cells leave the eyeball via the optic nerve (2) and pass through the optic chiasma (3), where some fibers cross to the opposite side and some fibers remain uncrossed. They terminate in the lateral geniculate body (6). Here they synapse with third-order neurons the axons of which pass to the visual centers of the cortex. The oculomotor nerve (n. III), responsible for pupillomotoric and accommodation reflexes, originates in the midbrain nuclei.

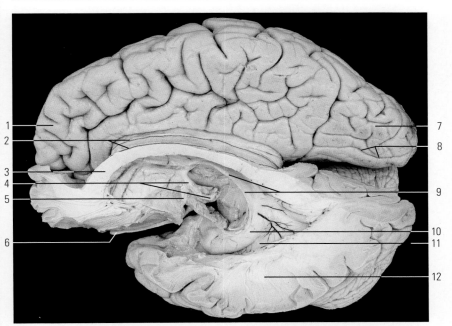

1 Frontal lobe of right hemisphere
2 Longitudinal striae
   (indusium griseum)
3 Corpus callosum
4 **Columna of fornix** and
   mamillary body
5 Anterior commissure
6 Olfactory bulb
7 Occipital lobe of right hemisphere
8 **Calcarine sulcus**
   (primary visual area of brain)
9 **Fornix**
   (on the roof of III. ventricle)
10 Hippocampus
11 Cornu inferius of lateral ventricle
12 Temporal lobe of left hemisphere
13 Optic chiasma
14 Caudate nucleus
15 **Thalamus**
16 Pineal body (diencephalon)
17 Colliculi of midbrain and cerebral
   aqueduct
18 Fourth ventricle
19 Pons
20 **Hypothalamus**
   (part of diencephalon)
21 Stalk of hypophysis
   (infundibulum) (connection with
   neurohypophysis)
22 Pituitary gland, anterior lobe
   (adenohypophysis)
23 Gyrus cinguli
   (continuous with hippocampus)
24 Uncus of hippocampus

Dissection of the limbic system and hippocampus in the left hemisphere. Note the spiral course of the fornix (4). The hippocampus (10) protrudes into the lateral ventricle of the temporal lobe (12).

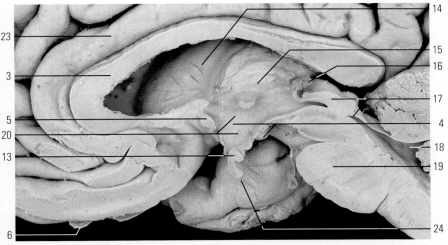

Midsagittal section through the brain showing the area of the hypothalamus (20). The lateral brain ventricle has been opened to display the caudate nucleus (14) and thalamus (15).

The **limbic system** forges links between the (unconscious) autonomic and the (conscious) central nervous system (cerebral cortex). It consists of a central area (amygdaloid nucleus, anterior thalamic nucleus, hypothalamic nuclei), and a ring of cortical structures, called the limbic cortex [hippocampal gyrus (10), cingulate gyrus, fornix (9) etc.]. It is associated with the emotional aspects of behavior and the responses of visceral organs that accompany emotions ("visceral brain") and brain mechanisms involved in short-term memory.

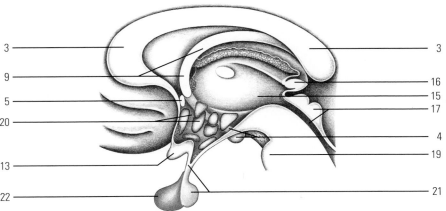

◄ **Area of the hypothalamus with hypothalamic nuclei** indicated in blue. Note the connection with the pituitary gland (neurohypophysis and infundibulum (21) (yellow). Green = nucleus supraopticus and paraventricularis, important for the regulation of water balance and smooth muscle tone, e.g., of uterus during delivery.

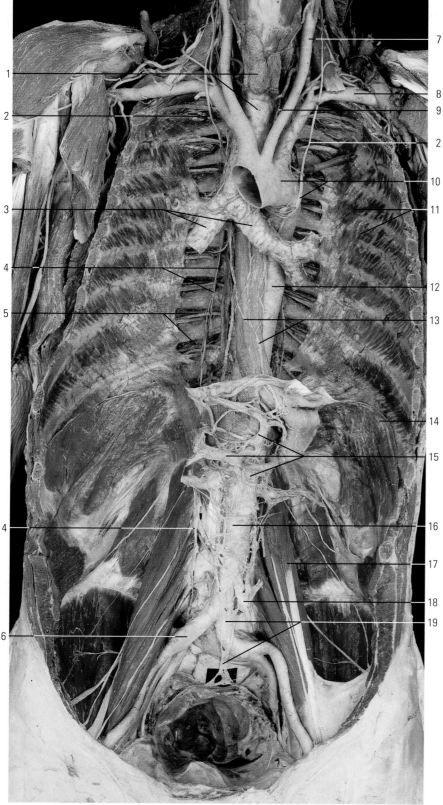

1 Thyroid gland and trachea
2 **Vagus nerve** (n. X)
3 Main bronchi
4 Sympathetic trunk with ganglia
5 Intercostal nerves
6 Common iliac artery
7 Common carotid artery
8 Subclavian artery
9 Recurrent laryngeal nerve
 (branch of vagus nerve)
10 Aortic arch with recurrent
 laryngeal nerve
11 Internal intercostal muscles
12 Thoracic part of the aorta
13 Vagus nerves at esophagus
14 Diaphragm
15 **Solar plexus** (comprising celiac
 and superior mesenteric ganglion)
16 Abdominal part of the aorta
17 Psoas major muscle
18 **Inferior mesenteric plexus**
 around the inferior mesenteric
 artery
19 **Superior hypogastric plexus**
20 Spinal cord (origin of
 sympathetic neurons, only present
 in C_8–L_3)
21 Spinal nerve
22 **Splanchnic nerves** (connection
 between sympathetic trunk and
 celiac ganglion)
23 Abdominal part of the esophagus
24 Superior laryngeal and cervical
 cardiac branches of the vagus nerve
25 **Inferior hypogastric plexus**
 (pelvic plexus)
26 Spinal cord with spinal nerves
 and dorsal root ganglia

Dissection of autonomic nervous system at the dorsal body wall. The sympathetic trunk (4) running parallel with the vertebral column represents part of the sympathetic system, whereas the vagus nerve (2) belongs to the parasympathetic system. Note the **solar plexus** (15), the most important center of the autonomic nervous system within the abdominal and pelvic cavities.

Zones of Head	
I	Diaphragm
II	Heart (also left arm and 5th finger)
III	Esophagus
IV	Stomach
V	Small intestine
VI	Colon
VII	Kidneys, testis/ovary
VIII	Urinary bladder
IX	Liver, gallbladder

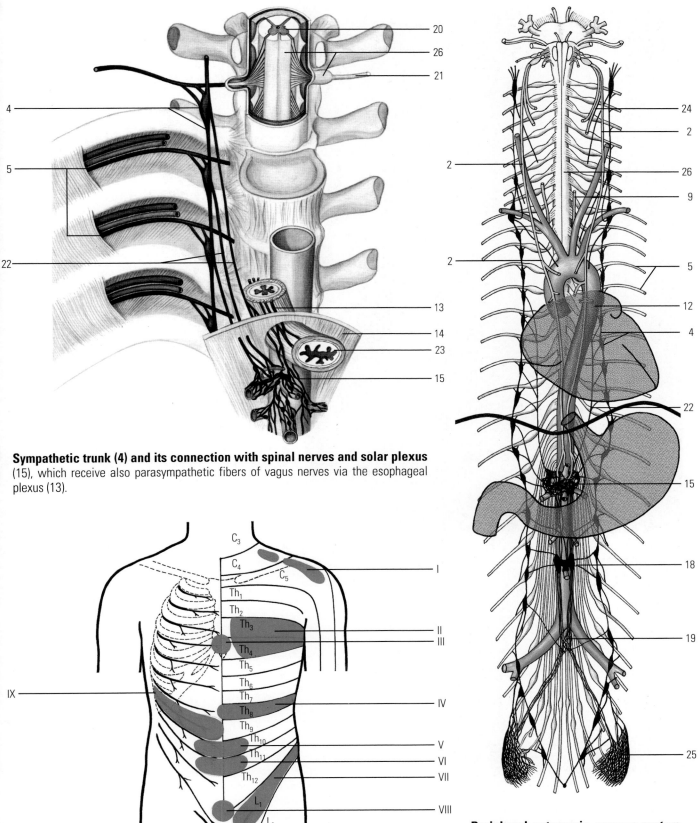

Sympathetic trunk (4) and its connection with spinal nerves and solar plexus
(15), which receive also parasympathetic fibers of vagus nerves via the esophageal plexus (13).

Head's zones (indicated in red). They represent skin areas that react hypersensitively in the event of internal organ diseases (C₃–C₅, Th₁–Th₁₂, L₁–L₃ = cutaneous segments).

Peripheral autonomic nervous system
(schematic drawing). Black = autonomic ganglia and sympathetic trunk (4); yellow = vagus nerve (2), containing parasympathetic fibers.

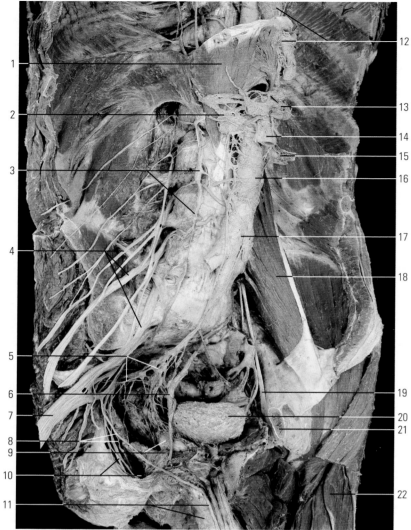

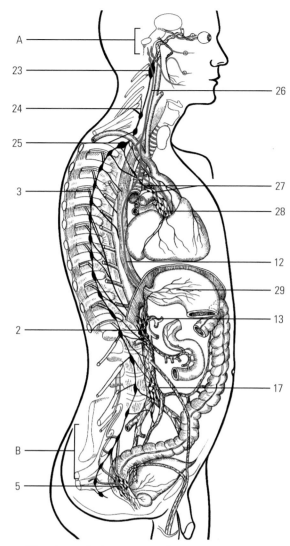

Autonomic ganglia and nerves at the dorsal body wall and within the pelvic cavity (male, antero-lateral view). Note the location of the solar plexus (2) and inferior hypogastric plexus (5), the latter is most important for autonomic innervation of genital organs.

Structure of the autonomic nervous system. Blue = vagus nerve (n. X); black = sympathetic trunk; A = cranial autonomic system (blue); B = sacral autonomic system (blue); A and B represent the parasympathicus.

1 Diaphragm
2 **Solar plexus**
3 Sympathetic trunk with ganglia
4 **Lumbosacral plexus** (Th$_{12}$–L$_5$, Co)
5 Inferior hypogastric plexus
6 Ureter and ductus deferens
7 **Sciatic nerve**
8 Pudendal nerves
9 Prostate gland
10 Levator ani muscle and fossa ischiorectalis with branches of pudendal nerve
11 Root of penis and dorsal nerve of penis
12 Esophagus with vagus nerves
13 **Celiac ganglion**
14 **Superior mesenteric artery** and **plexus** (13 + 14 represent the main autonomic innervation of abdominal organs)

15 Renal artery and renal plexus
16 Aorta with autonomic nervous plexus
17 **Inferior mesenteric artery** and **plexus**
18 Psoas major muscle
19 Obturator nerve
20 Bladder (vesica urinaria)
21 Pubic bone (cut)
22 Muscles of the thigh
23 **Superior cervical ganglion** (sympathetic innervation of the head)
24 Sympathetic trunk of the neck with three ganglia
25 Cervicothoracic or stellate ganglion (sympathetic innervation of upper extremity)
26 **Vagus nerve** (containing parasympathetic nerve fibers)
27 Bronchopulmonary plexus
28 Cardiac plexus
29 Gastric plexus

Glossary

Abdomen – The area between diaphragm and pelvis

Abduction – Movement away from the midline

Acetabulum – The rounded cavity on the external surface of the innominate bone that receives the head of the femur

Adduction – Movement toward the midline

Alveolus – Small sac or pouch, e.g. in the lung (pl. alveoli, adj. alveolar)

Amphiarthrosis – Articulation, midway between diarthrosis and synarthrosis

Ampulla – A sac-like dilatation of a canal

Anulus – Ring

Apex – The pointed end of a conical structure

Aponeurosis – Broad sheet-like layer of connective tissue forming a muscle tendon

Aqueduct – A canal or passage, especially for the conduction of a liquid

Arteriole – Small artery

Artery – Vessel that carries blood away from the heart

Articulation – Joint

Atrium – A cavity or sinus, e.g., the upper chamber of the heart (adj. atrial)

Axilla – Hollow beneath the arm, the armpit

Bronchiole – Terminal branch of a bronchus

Bronchus – Large air passageway in the lung (pl. bronchi)

Buccal – Pertaining to the check or mouth

Bursa – A sac or pouch of synovial fluid located at friction points, especially about joints

Canaliculus – A small channel or canal

Capillary – Microscopic blood vessel

Cataract – Loss of transparency of the crystalline lens of the eye

Cephalic – Pertaining to the head

Cerebrum – Largest part of the brain

Cervix – Neck (adj. cervical)

Chiasma – Crossing, e.g., of the optic nerves

Choana – Funnel–shaped, like the posterior openings of the nasal fossa

Colliculi – Small elevations

Choroid – Middle layer of the eye

Cortex – Outer layer of an organ (adj. cortical)

Dens – Tooth (pl. dentes)

Diaphysis – Shaft of a long bone

Diarthrosis – Freely movable joint (synovial joint)

Diastole – Relaxation phase of the cardiac cycle

Duct – Tube or vessel

Efferent – Carrying impulses away from a center

Embryo – Developing offspring during the first three months of pregnancy

Epiphysis – End of a long bone

Epithelial tissue – The tissue that forms glands, or the outer part of the skin. It lines the mucous membranes or ducts

Esophagus – Tube that carries food from the oral cavity to the stomach

Extension – Stretching motion that increases the angle between bones and a joint

Falciform – Sickle-shaped

Fascia – A fibrous membrane covering or separating muscles or organs

Fenestra – Window

Fetus – A developing offspring after the third month of pregnancy to birth

Fissure – Deep groove

Flexion – Bending motion that decreases the angle between bones and a joint

Foramen – Opening or passageway (pl. foramina)

Fossa – Hollow or depression, as in a bone (pl. fossae)

Fovea – Small pit or cup-shaped depression (pl. foveae)

Ganglion – Collection of nerve cell bodies located outside the central nervous system (pl. ganglia)

Glomerulus – Cluster of capillaries (adj. glomerular)

Glossus – Tongue (adj. glossal)

Gyrus – Raised area of the cerebral cortex (pl. gyri)

Hepar – Liver (adj. hepatic)

Hernia – The protrusion or projection of an organ through the wall of the cavity containing it

Hiatus – An opening; a foramen

Hilus – Area where vessels or nerves enter or leave an organ (pl. hili)

Hypophysis – Pituitary gland

Inguinal – Pertaining to the groin

Insertion – Place of attachment of a muscle to the bone that it moves

In situ – In position

Isthmus – A narrow passage connecting two large parts

Lacuna – A small, hollow space (pl. lacunae)

Ligament – Band of fibrous connective tissue that connects a bone to another bone or structure

Lordosis – Anterior convexity of the vertebral column

Lumen – The space within a tube or vessel

Lymphatics – Vessels that conduct lymph fluid

Mastication – Act of chewing

Mediastinum – Region between the lungs

Medulla – Inner region of an organ, marrow

Meninges – Fibrous membranes that cover the brain and spinal cord

Mesentery – The membranous peritoneal ligament that attached the small intestine to the dorsal abdominal wall

Myocardium – Heart muscle

Orifice – Any aperture or opening

Origin – Source, beginning; end of a muscle attached to a nonmoving part

Os – Bone (adj. osseous)

Ostium – A small opening

Pancreas – Large gland behind the stomach (adj. pancreatic)

Papilla – Small nipple-like projection or elevation

Parietal – Pertaining to the wall of a space or cavity

Perineum – Pelvic floor, external region between the anus and genital organs (adj. perineal)

Periosteum – Connective tissue membrane covering a bone

Peritoneum – Serous membrane that lines the abdominal cavity and forms the outer layer of the abdominal organs

Pharynx – Throat

Plexus – Network of vessels or nerves (pl. plexus)

Pleura – Serous membrane covering the lung and the chest

Proximal – Nearer to the point of origine or to a reference point

Pulmo – Lung (adj. pulmonary)

Ramus – Branch of a nerve or vessel (pl. rami)

Ren – Kidney (adj. renal)

Septum – A connective tissue wall or membrane dividing two cavities

Serosa – Serous membrane

Sinus – A hollow in a bone or other tissue, a channel for blood

Sphincter – A circular muscle constricting an orifice

Spleen – Lymphoid organ behind the stomach (adj. splenic)

Sulcus – Shallow groove (pl. sulci)

Synarthrosis – Immovable joint

Synovia – Lubricating fluid found in joints or bursae

Tendon – Cord of fibrous connective tissue that attached a muscle to a bone

Testis – Male reproductive gland (pl. testes)

Thorax – Chest (adj. thoracic)

Thyroid – Endocrine gland in the neck

Tonsil – Mass of lymphoid tissue in the region of the pharynx

Trachea – The windpipe, the tube, extending from the larynx to the bronchi (adj. tracheal)

Umbilical – Pertaining to the umbilicus or navel

Ureter – Tube that carries urine from the kidney to the urinary bladder

Urethra – Tube that carries urine from the urinary bladder to the outside of the body

Uterus – Muscular organ in the female pelvis within which the fetus develops

Uvula – Part of the soft palate

Valve – Structure that prevents fluid from flowing backward as in the heart or veins

Vas – A vessel or duct

Vein – Vessel that carries blood toward the heart

Venous sinus – Large channel that drains venous blood

Ventricle – Cavity or chamber; e.g. ventricles of the heart or brain (adj. ventricular)

Venule – Very small vein

Vertebra – A bone of the spinal column

Vesicle – Small sac or blister filled with fluid

Viscera – Internal organs inside the ventral body cavity

White matter – Nervous tissue composed of myelinated fibers

Xiphoid – Sword-shaped

Index